# Frank Schaffer's Biology for Everyday

Written by David Thurlo

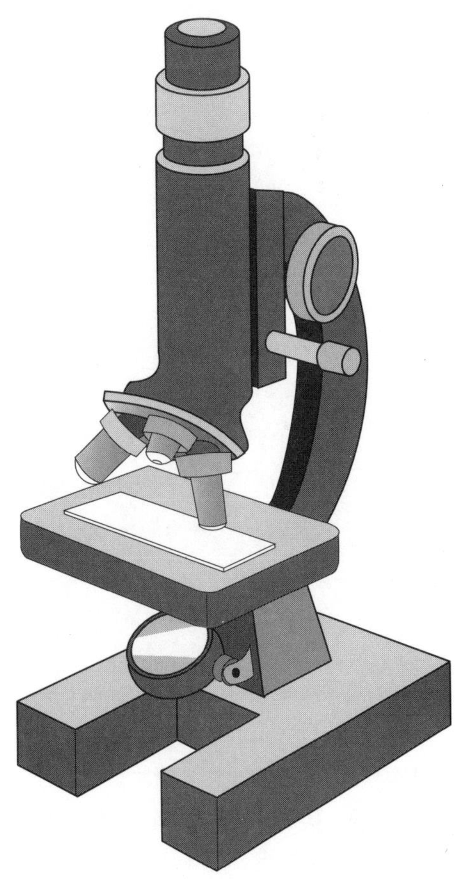

Copyeditors: Cindy Barden and Jason Eidinger

Interior Design: Good Neighbor Press, Inc.

Cover Illustration: Kent Publishing

FS110625 Frank Schaffer's Biology for Everyday

23740 Hawthorne Blvd.
Torrance, CA 90505

# Table of Contents

# Introduction

*Frank Schaffer's Biology for Everyday* contains a wealth of interesting activities students can complete to learn more about important topics in biology. Topics covered in this book include characteristics of living things, the chemistry of biology, cell structure and function, ecology and the environment, animals (arthropods, echinoderms, reptiles, mammals), vitamins, diseases and microbes, and classification.

Easy to use and self-explanatory, most of these reproducible activities can be completed by the students at their desks using textbook references. Others require access to materials like encyclopedias and magazines usually found in the classroom. Often activities reinforce each other, allowing more in-depth work, some of which may be done at home or in a laboratory setting. Several hands-on activities require students to carry out simple investigations using inexpensive equipment and supplies usually found in science storerooms.

Most activities (crossword puzzles, vocabulary matching, chart making, and graphing ) may be conducted individually, though a few require small group work and data sharing. Many of the activities are suitable for homework and/or non-instructional time, where the student takes responsibility for carrying out the tasks without assistance.

Whether you use these materials to supplement your biology class, give students an opportunity to reinforce their basic knowledge and scientific skills, or just make science more interesting for the learner, you'll find the biology activities in this book useful and relevant to your objectives.

# Biology References


Kenneth R. Miller, Joseph Levine, *Biology, New Edition* (Englewood Cliffs, NJ, 1993)

Peter Alexander, Mary J. Bahret, Judith Chaves, Gary Courts, Naomi Skolky D'Alessio, *Biology* (Morristown, NJ, Silver Burdett, 1986)

Stanley L. Weinberg, Abraham Kalish, *Biology: An Inquiry into the Nature of Life* (Boston, MA, Allyn and Bacon, 1972)

Charles H. Heimler, *Focus on Life Science* (Columbus, OH, Merrill, 1987)

William L. Ramsey, Lucretia A. Gabriel, James F. McGuirk, Clifford R. Phillips, Frank M. Watenpaugh, *Life Science* (New York, NY, Holt, Rinehart and Winston, 1986)

William J. Cromie, William H. Amos, *Secrets of the Seas* (Plesantville, NY, Reader's Digest, 1972)

Anthea Maton, et al, *Ecology, Earth's Natural Resources* (Englewood Cliffs, NJ, Prentice Hall, 1993)

Anthea Maton, et al, *Cells, Building Blocks of Life* (Englewood Cliffs, NJ, Prentice Hall, 1993)

Anthea Maton, et al, *Ecology, Earth's Living Resources* (Englewood Cliffs, NJ, Prentice Hall, 1993)

Anthea Maton, et al, *Parade of Life, Monerans, Protists, Fungi, and Plants* (Englewood Cliffs, NJ, Prentice Hall, 1993)

Dale T. Hesser, Susan S. Leach, *Focus on Earth Science* (Columbus, OH, Merril, 1987)

Name ______________________________ Date ______________

# Characteristics of Living Things

Living organisms have certain characteristics that place them apart from nonliving things. The most common of those characteristics are listed in Table A. Write a definition or description of each characteristic, then give an example of each characteristic. The first characteristic is done for you.

**Table A**

| Characteristic | Definition or description | Example |
|---|---|---|
| 1. REPRODUCTION | produce new organisms like themselves | cow giving birth to calf |
| 2. NUTRITION | | |
| 3. RESPOND TO ENVIRONMENT | | |
| 4. CONSISTS OF CELLS | | |
| 5. RESPIRATION | | |
| 6. ADAPTATION | | |
| 7. INTAKE OF MATERIALS | | |
| 8. GROWTH | | |
| 9. MOVEMENT | | |
| 10. EXCRETION | | |
| 11. SYNTHESIS OR SECRETION | | |
| 12. REGULATION | | |

Name ______________________ Date ____________

FRANK SCHAFFER'S **BIOLOGY FOR EVERYDAY**

# Communication in Biology

Match the word part (prefix or suffix) with its meaning by writing the letter of the correct meaning in the blank.

| **Word Parts** | **Word Meanings** |
|---|---|
| 1. ____ autos- | A. self |
| 2. ____ bio- | B. cell |
| 3. ____ -cide | C. on, above |
| 4. ____ cyto- | D. animals |
| 5. ____ -dermis | E. first |
| 6. ____ epi- | F. nerve |
| 7. ____ exo- | G. life |
| 8. ____ hemi- | H. killer |
| 9. ____ herba- | I. within |
| 10. ____ histo- | J. study of |
| 11. ____ intra- | K. dry |
| 12. ____ -logy | L. one |
| 13. ____ macro- | M. large |
| 14. ____ micro- | N. plant |
| 15. ____ mono- | O. skin |
| 16. ____ neur- | P. outside of |
| 17. ____ osteo- | Q. bone |
| 18. ____ proto- | R. small |
| 19. ____ xero- | S. tissue |
| 20. ____ zoo- | T. half |

Combine prefixes and suffixes from above to write five words. Explain what each word means. Which of the words you wrote are already used by scientists?

Name ______________________ Date ______________

FRANK SCHAFFER'S **BIOLOGY FOR EVERYDAY**

# Measuring Lengths Metrically

**Supplies needed:** graph paper, meterstick and/or metric ruler

Measure the lengths of the lines below. Express your answers in both millimeters and centimeters. Be accurate to within one millimeter.

1. ______________
2. ____________
3. ________________________
4. ____________________________________________
5. ____________________
6. ________________________________
7. ________________________________________
8. _____________________________________________________
9. _______
10. ________________
11. ______________________________
12. ___________________________________________________
13. _______________________________________________
14. ____
15. ____________________________________________________________
16. The length of this paper is ________cm.
17. The thickness of your textbook is ________mm.
18. The length of your tabletop or desk is __________cm.
19. The distance diagonally across the desk or table is______cm.
20. The volume of your textbook is ____________$cm^3$.
21. The room's length is _________meters.
22. The room's width is _________meters.
23. The height of the room is ______meters.
24. You are _________cm tall.
25. Construct a line graph of the following data. Use "dots" to indicate boys and "x's" to indicate girls.
    A. Boys' height from shortest to tallest.
    B. Girls' height from shortest to tallest.

Name ____________________ Date ____________

**FRANK SCHAFFER'S BIOLOGY FOR EVERYDAY**

# The Chemistry of Biology

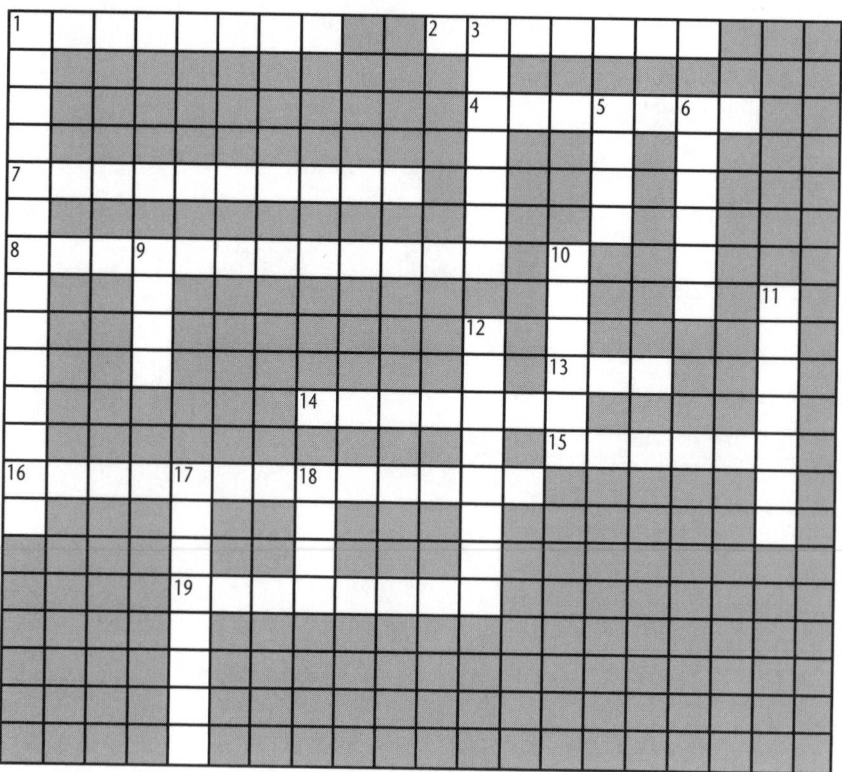


**Across**

1. one or more atoms covalently bonded
2. two or more substances mixed but not chemically combined
4. compounds that contain carbon
7. a heterogeneous mixture containing particles distributed within a gas, liquid, or solid
8. organic compound containing carbon, hydrogen, and oxygen
13. an atom that has gained or lost one or more electrons
14. a mixture composed of particles dispersed in a medium
15. the substance that is dissolved
16. made up of two sugars
19. substances resulting from a chemical reaction

**Down**

1. a single sugar
3. atoms of the same element with different mass numbers
5. the smallest particle of an element that retains the properties of that element
6. compounds with the same molecular formula but different molecular structures
9. produces hydroxide ions in a water solution
10. organic compounds that store energy
11. matter that contains only one kind of atom
12. large, complex organic compounds containing carbon, hydrogen, oxygen, and nitrogen
17. formed by the chemical combination of two or more elements
18. produces hydrogen ions in a water solution

Name ____________________ Date ____________

FRANK SCHAFFER'S **BIOLOGY FOR EVERYDAY**

# Forming Organic Bonds

The following simple diagrams reveal the number of covalent bonds formed by hydrogen, oxygen, nitrogen, and carbon.

hydrogen
(1 bond)

oxygen
(2 bonds)

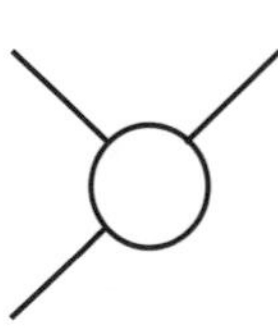

nitrogen
(3 bonds)

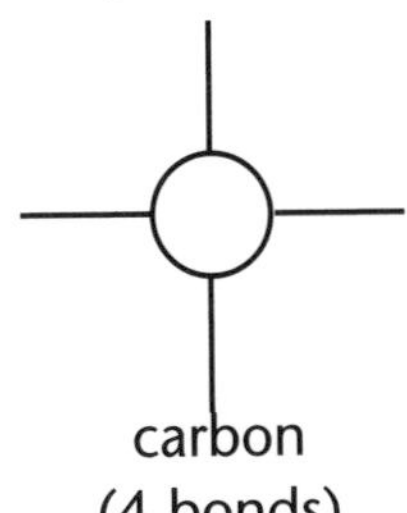

carbon
(4 bonds)

The structural formula for water, $H_2O$, is H–O–H

Using water as an example, draw structural formulas for the following organic compounds. Each compound possesses only single covalent bonds.

1. methane–$CH_4$
2. ammonia–$NH_3$
3. ethane–$C_2H_6$
4. propane–$C_3H_8$
5. pentane–$C_5H_{12}$
6. methyl amine–$CNH_5$
7. butane–$C_4H_{10}$
8. octane–$C_8H_{18}$
9. methyl ether–$C_2H_6O$
10. hexane–$C_6H_{14}$

Name ____________________ Date ____________

FRANK SCHAFFER'S **BIOLOGY FOR EVERYDAY**

# Cell Structure and Function

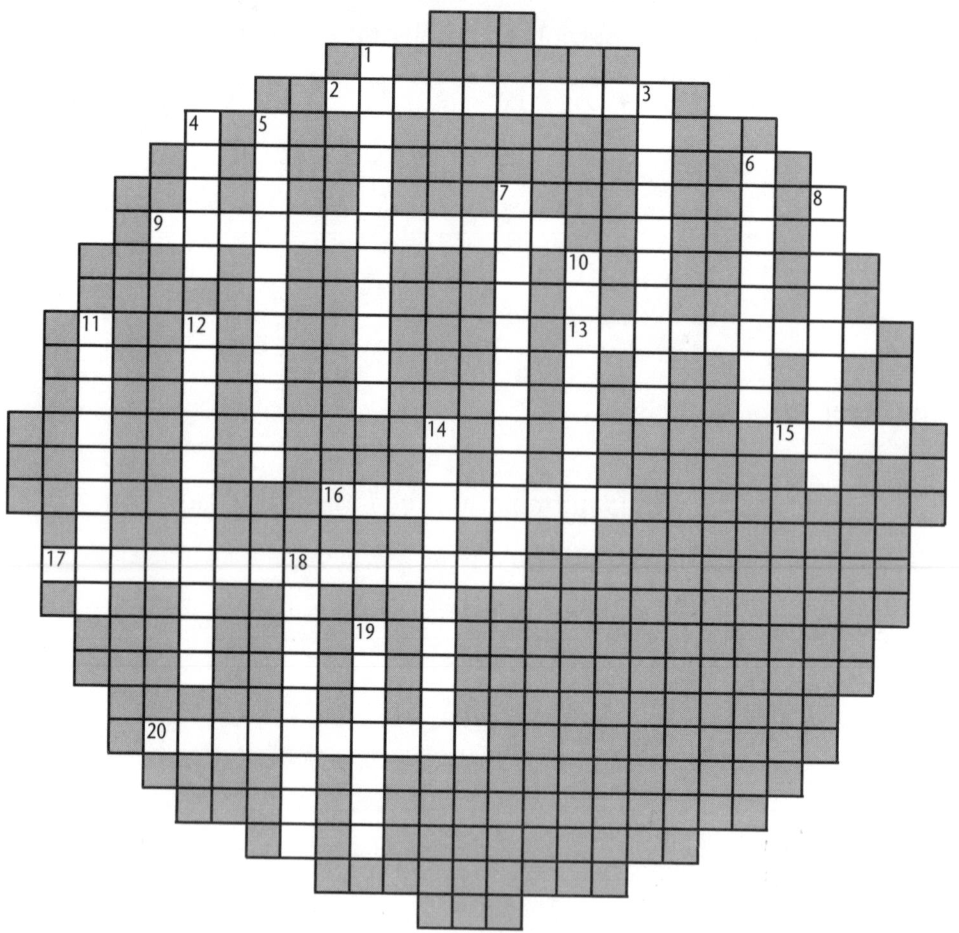


**Across**

2. thread-like structures containing the genetic material
9. the powerhouses of the cell
13. another name for the jelly-like material within cells
15. the basic unit of living things
16. a large tail-like structure which aids in cell motion
17. very thin thread-like fibers which help keep cell material flowing
20. the living material inside cells

**Down**

1. the organelle in which the food-making processes of plants take place
3. cells of plants, animals, and fungi are in this group
4. hair-like structures which aid in motion
5. a plastid that contains color pigments
6. fluid filled structures in cells
7. hollow pipe-like structures that help give a cell its shape
8. the organelles where proteins are made
10. stores and makes RNA in the nucleus
11. a nuclear material made of protein and DNA
12. the oldest known forms of life
14. cell structures that carry out special functions
18. contains digestive enzymes
19. the cell structure that controls activities

Name ____________________ Date ____________

FRANK SCHAFFER'S **BIOLOGY FOR EVERYDAY**

# Comparing Cells

Living things are made up of fundamental units called cells. Some simple organisms are made up of only one cell. Currently, cells are divided into two basic groups.

Those that contain specialized membrane-enclosed organelles, the eukaryotes (plants, animals, and fungi).

Those that do not contain membrane-enclosed organelles, the prokaryotes (bacteria).

Complete the chart. List cell structures and their functions for the two basic groups, eukaryotes and prokaryotes.

| Prokaryotes | | Eukaryotes | | | |
|---|---|---|---|---|---|
| Bacteria | | Plants | | Animals | |
| **Structure** | **Function** | **Structure** | **Function** | **Structure** | **Function** |
| cell wall | gives rigidity | cell wall | gives rigidity | none | none |
| | | | | | |
| | | | | | |
| | | | | | |
| | | | | | |
| | | | | | |
| | | | | | |

Name ______________________________ Date ______________

FRANK SCHAFFER'S **BIOLOGY FOR EVERYDAY**

# Basic Chemistry in Living Cells

Every living cell depends on special chemical reactions in order to survive, grow, and carry out its life functions. Match the term or reaction in the left column with the letter of its best definition or description from the column on the right.

1. ____ active site
2. ____ anabolic reaction
3. ____ autotroph
4. ____ catabolic reaction
5. ____ catalyst
6. ____ dehydration
7. ____ denaturation
8. ____ enzyme
9. ____ exergonic reaction
10. ____ fermentation
11. ____ heterotroph
12. ____ hydrolysis
13. ____ photosynthesis
14. ____ respiration
15. ____ substrate

A. living things that make their own food

B. living things that must take in food from another source

C. when simple substances join to form more complex substances

D. when complex substances are broken down into simpler substances

E. an anabolic reaction which involves the removal of water

F. a catabolic reaction which synthesis involves the addition of water

G. a reaction that releases energy

H. a substance that controls the rate of a chemical reaction without itself being altered or used up

I. protein that acts as a catalyst

J. the surface on which an enzyme acts

K. a special region of an enzyme that can join with a substrate

L. this may alter the active site in an enzyme

M. the breakdown of glucose to release energy in which the final electron acceptor is inorganic

N. the breakdown of glucose and the release of energy in which the final electron acceptor is organic

O. when light energy is changed to chemical energy in the form of glucose

Name ______________________________ Date ______________

# Factors Affecting Photosynthesis: Part 1

The rate of photosynthesis may vary depending on factors like light intensity and temperature. Use the data in Table A to construct a line graph indicating the relationship between light intensity and the rate of photosynthesis. The scales on the graph are labeled.

**Table A**

| LIGHT INTENSITY (Thousands of lumens) | RATE OF PHOTOSYNTHESIS (percentage) |
|---|---|
| 1 | 7 |
| 2 | 12 |
| 3 | 17 |
| 4 | 24 |
| 5 | 29 |
| 6 | 33 |
| 7 | 38 |
| 8 | 42 |
| 9 | 44 |
| 10 | 45 |
| 11 | 45 |
| 12 | 45 |
| 13 | 45 |
| 14 | 45 |
| 15 | 45 |

**Graph A**

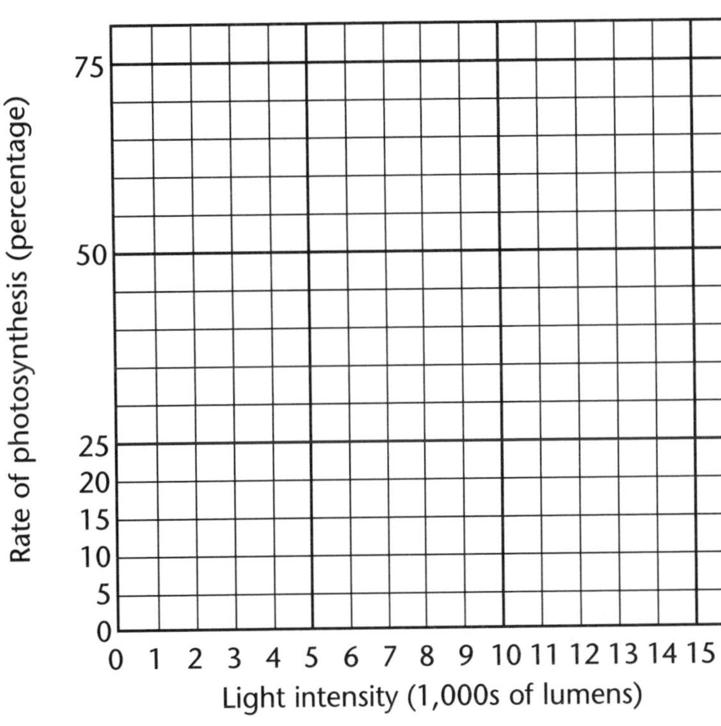


1. What happens to Graph A after the light intensity reaches 10,000 lumens?

2. What could explain this?

Name ______________________________ Date ____________

FRANK SCHAFFER'S **BIOLOGY FOR EVERYDAY**

# Factors Affecting Photosynthesis: Part 2

Use the data in Table B to graph the relationship between temperature and the rate of photosynthesis. Complete the scale using the graph on the previous page as a guide.

**Table B**

| TEMPERATURE (°C) | RATE OF PHOTOSYNTHESIS (percentage) |
|---|---|
| 2 | 11 |
| 4 | 13 |
| 6 | 14 |
| 8 | 15 |
| 10 | 16 |
| 12 | 17 |
| 14 | 19 |
| 16 | 22 |
| 18 | 24 |
| 20 | 28 |
| 22 | 32 |
| 24 | 35 |
| 26 | 40 |
| 28 | 46 |
| 30 | 55 |
| 32 | 70 |
| 34 | 75 |
| 36 | 72 |
| 38 | 50 |
| 40 | 15 |

**Graph B**

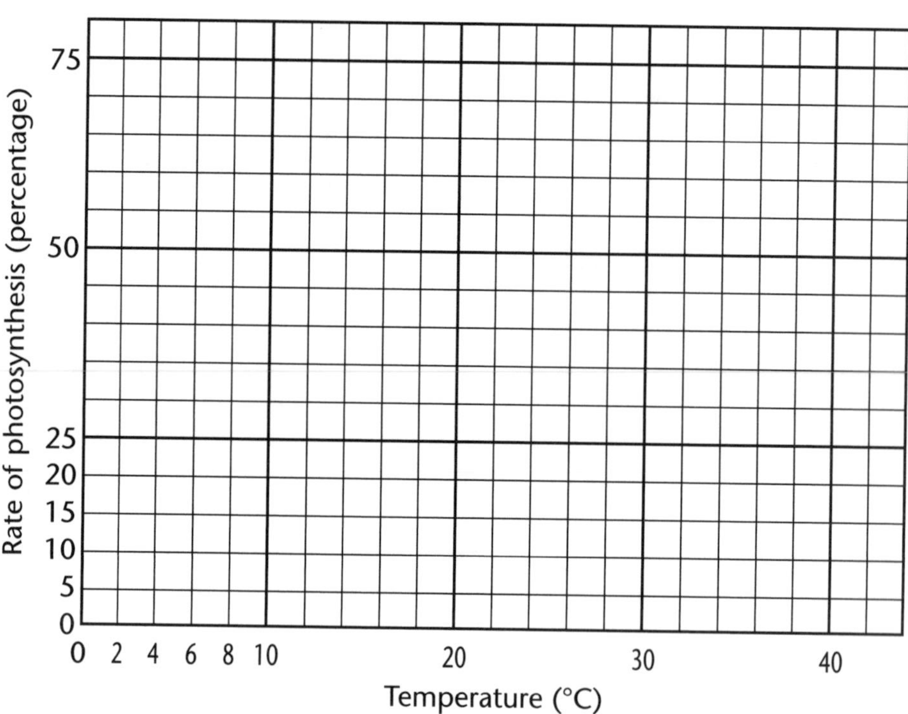


1. Describe both graphs.

2. Explain the shape of Graph B in relation to temperature.

3. What happens to photosynthesis after 34°C?

4. What could explain this?

# Comparing Earth's Biomes

The biosphere can be divided into large regions called biomes, which are areas with distinct combinations of plants and animals. The greatest factor in determining the type of biome is climate. The types of plants present are a key element in identifying the biome. Complete the biome chart to compare the earth's biomes.

| | **Tundra** | **Coniferous Forest** | **Deciduous Forest** | **Tropical Rain Forest** | **Grassland** | **Desert** |
|---|---|---|---|---|---|---|
| 1. average rainfall | | | | | | |
| 2. average temperature | | | | | | |
| 3. location | | | | | | |
| 4. typical plants | | | | | | |
| 5. typical animals | | | | | | |
| 6. other features | | | | | | |

Name ______________________________ Date ______________



# Are You a Bird-Brain?

Listed below are several terms referring to the class Aves. Though this class has certain traits similar to those of Reptilia, there are many differences. Match the term in the left column with the definition or description in the right column.

1. ____ albumen
2. ____ barbs
3. ____ barbules
4. ____ birds
5. ____ contour
6. ____ chalaza
7. ____ crop
8. ____ down feathers
9. ____ filoplumes
10. ____ gizzard
11. ____ keel
12. ____ quill
13. ____ rachis
14. ____ syrinx
15. ____ tail gland

A. warm-blooded invertebrate with feathers and wings

B. the hollow part of a feather that extends below the skin

C. solid exposed part of a feather shaft

D. the extensions of a feather's shaft

E. tiny hooked branches connecting feathers barbs

F. short, fluffy feathers

G. sparsely scattered feathers with a long shaft and a few barbs

H. the large feathers that give a bird's body its outline

I. secretes an oily fluid that helps smooth feathers

J. the breastbone where the large flight muscles are attached

K. where birds store and soften food with mucus

L. second part of the stomach, where the food is ground up

M. the voice box of a bird

N. a watery solution of protein surrounding the yolk

O. dense cords of albumen that help keep the yolk and embryo in place

Name ______________________ Date ______________

# Mammals: Groups and Traits

**Across**

2. small mammals adapted to eating small invertebrates
7. all small herbivores with chisel-shaped front teeth
9. a mammal that lays eggs
10. meat-eating mammals
11. mammals adapted to ocean life
12. the types, number, and arrangement of teeth
15. hoofed mammals
16. plant-eating mammals
17. the most primitive mammals to bear their young alive
18. when the embryo is in the uterus of the mother
19. a muscular organ in mammals where the embryo develops

**Down**

1. a mammal's coat of hair
3. a means of sensing the environment by using sound
4. mammals with very reduced teeth or none at all
5. a specialized organ connecting the mother's and embryo's blood
6. small, mainly herbivorous mammals with sharp, chisel shaped front teeth
8. a mammal that eats both plants and animals
12. a specialized muscle that helps increase lung capacity
13. an endothermic vertebrate with hair that provides milk
14. mammals with large brains, depth perception, grasping hands, and special agility

Name ______________________ Date ______________

# Bird Adaptations

Perhaps the most outstanding characteristic of the class Aves is the ability to fly. This ability doesn't come without special adaptations, however. Answer the following questions, in detail, concerning bird adaptations.

1. Explain what adaptations internally and externally allow most birds to fly.

2. Describe the three main types of bird feathers. Draw a feather, labeling its parts.

3. What are some other adaptations other than flight that birds have made?

Name ______________________________ Date ______________



# Mammal Behavior

Most mammals are very active. All need to maintain a constant body temperature. This requires a plentiful food supply and special adaptations to changing environmental conditions. Several behavioral adaptations mammals have made to increase the survival chances of their species are listed below. Explain and define each adaptation. Give examples of animals that carry out that particular behavior.

1. migration

2. hibernation

3. territoriality

4. social hierarchy

5. courtship behavior

6. communication

Name ______________________________ Date ______________

# Vertebrate Comparisons

Although they have a lot in common, vertebrate animals include a large and diverse group of living organisms. They have the same basic biological functions and needs, but carry them out in unique ways. Describe the similarities and differences between different vertebrates with the following body systems.

1. skeletal systems

2. muscular systems

3. integumentary systems

4. digestive systems

5. circulatory systems

6. gas exchange systems

Name ______________________ Date ____________

FRANK SCHAFFER'S **BIOLOGY FOR EVERYDAY**

# Them Bones

There are 206 bones in the human body. It is a relatively simple task to learn to identify many of them. One step toward learning to identify them is to first associate the bones with a body part, like the arm or leg.

Six body parts are listed below. Match the letters of the bones with the appropriate body parts. Some bones may be associated with more than one body part.

1. arm: ________
2. leg: ________
3. foot: ________
4. hand: ________
5. head: ________
6. torso: ________

| | | | | |
|---|---|---|---|---|
| A. carpals | D. fibula | G. metatarsals | J. radius | M. tarsals |
| B. cranium | E. humerus | H. patella | K. rib | N. tibia |
| C. femur | F. metacarpals | I. phalanges | L. scapula | O. ulna |

# The Human Body: Skeleton and Major Tissues

The human body is made up of specialized tissues, including those of the bones, organs, and muscles. Answer the following questions about the human body structure.

1. What four types of tissues make up the human body?
2. What are the two divisions of the skeleton?
3. What happens during the process of ossification?
4. What are the major components of bone?
5. Name the three types of muscle tissue.
6. How do the bones of the joints move?
7. Describe muscle fibers. What is the mechanism of muscle contraction?
8. Where does the energy for muscle contraction come from?
9. What are the two main layers of skin?
10. What are the five functions of the skin?

# Take Your Vitamins

Vitamins are an important class of nutrients found in foods. Many vitamins are co-enzymes and are therefore essential for normal cell functions. Water soluble B and C vitamins can be lost if cooked in water and excess amounts are released from the body. The other vitamins are fat soluble and can only be absorbed if eaten along with fats or oils. Excess fat soluble vitamins are stored in the body.

Complete the chart on vitamins.

| Vitamin | Common name | Function or need | Sources |
|---|---|---|---|
| 1. $B_1$ | | | |
| 2. $B_2$ | | | |
| 3. $B_3$ | | | |
| 4. $B_{12}$ | | | |
| 5. C | | | |
| 6. A | | | |
| 7. D | | | |
| 8. E | | | |
| 9. K | | | |

Name ______________________ Date ______________

FRANK SCHAFFER'S **BIOLOGY FOR EVERYDAY**

# Mineral Wealth and Health

Minerals are elements needed for the normal functioning of the body. Minerals are obtained by eating the right kinds of foods. Only small amounts of minerals are needed for most people to maintain their health.

The major functions of ten common minerals are listed below. Name the mineral from the list below that is responsible for each function. List food sources for each mineral.

1. Function: Synthesis of insulin, component of some enzymes = __________ Food sources:

2. Function: Formation of hemoglobin = __________
   Food sources:

3. Function: Fluid balance, acid-base balance, synthesis of stomach acid = __________ Food sources:

4. Function: Fluid balance regulation, maintains ionic balance, nerve impulse transmission = __________
   Food sources:

5. Function: Cofactor for enzymes that regulate muscle and nerve function = __________ Food sources:

6. Function: Formation of thyroxin, which regulates metabolism = __________ Food sources:

7. Function: Formation of hemoglobin in red blood cells, cellular respiration = __________ Food sources:

8. Function: Nerve and muscle function, regulation of heartbeat, fluid balance = __________
   Food sources:

9. Function: Bone and teeth formation, formation of lipids in cell membranes, ATP, nucleic acids =
   __________ Food sources:

10. Function: Bone and teeth formation, muscle contraction, blood clotting, nerve impulses =
    __________ Food sources:

**Minerals:** calcium, chlorine, copper, iodine, iron, magnesium, phosphorus, potassium, sodium, zinc

Name ______________________ Date ______________

# Lunch From the Inside

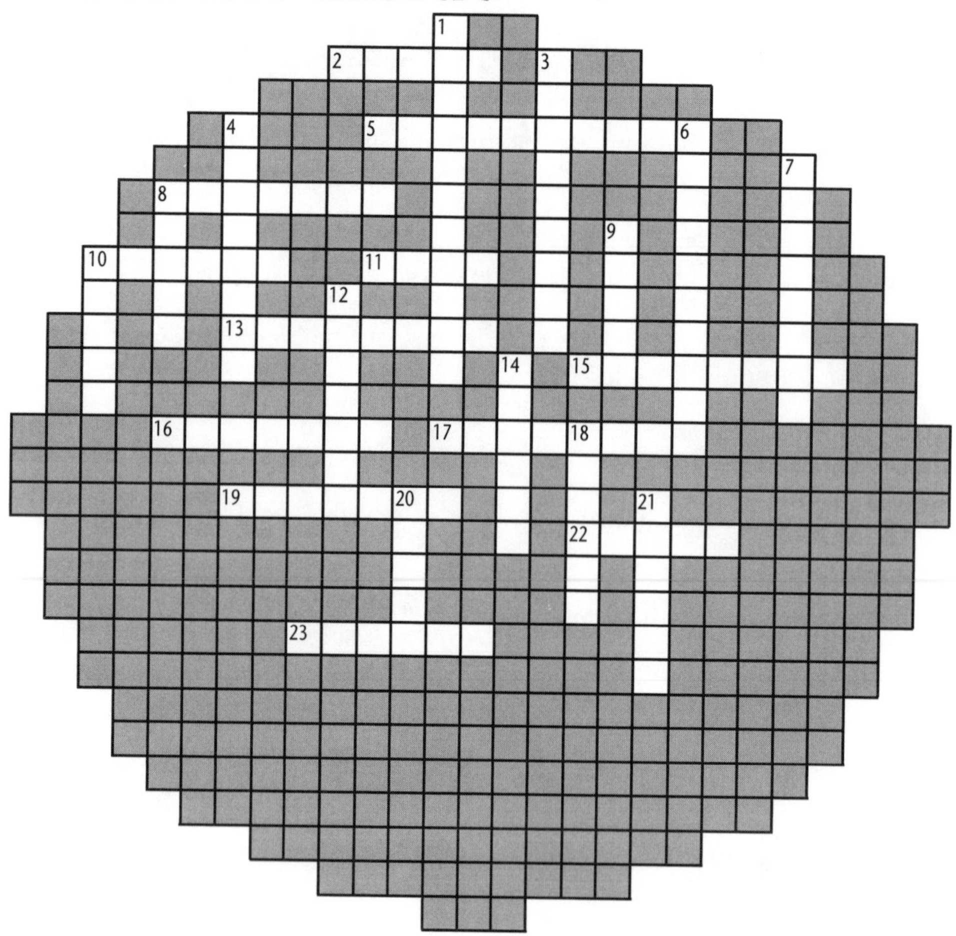


**Across**

2. the largest gland in the body
5. a flap of tissue that closes off the windpipe during swallowing
8. teeth used for tearing food
10. teeth well adapted for crushing and grinding food
11. from the liver, aids in digestion of fats
13. a small tube connected to the cecum
15. a bone-like substance covering the tooth root
16. the region behind the mouth where swallowing begins
17. teeth used for biting and cutting food
19. a pouch-like enlargement of the digestive tube
22. the last part of the small intestine
23. a calcium-containing substance that protects teeth

**Down**

1. a series of rhythmic muscular contractions that moves food along
3. the muscular tube connecting the pharynx to the stomach
4. produces hormones and pancreatic juice
6. circular muscles that close a tube when they contract
7. the first part of the small intestine
8. contains many bacteria that feed on undigested waste
9. the fluid mixture of food and gastric juice
10. contains taste buds and salivary glands
12. the middle of the small intestine
14. the final part of the large intestine
18. a digestive juice that helps lubricate food
20. the first part of the large intestine
21. a bone-like substance surrounding the pulp cavity

Name ______________________ Date ______________

# The Composition and Functions of Blood

Explain in detail the composition and function of red blood cells, white blood cells (all three types), plasma, and platelets. Mention which organs are involved with these blood elements.

1. Red blood cells

2. White blood cells

3. Plasma

4. Platelets

# Just Your Type

In the early nineteenth century scientists discovered that there are four major blood types: A, B, AB, and O. Explain how these four blood types were discovered and how blood typing is done. Tell what type of blood a person can receive in a transfusion and what the Rh factor is. Write your answers on the back of this page.

Name ______________________ Date ______________

FRANK SCHAFFER'S **BIOLOGY FOR EVERYDAY**

# Don't Waste Your Breath

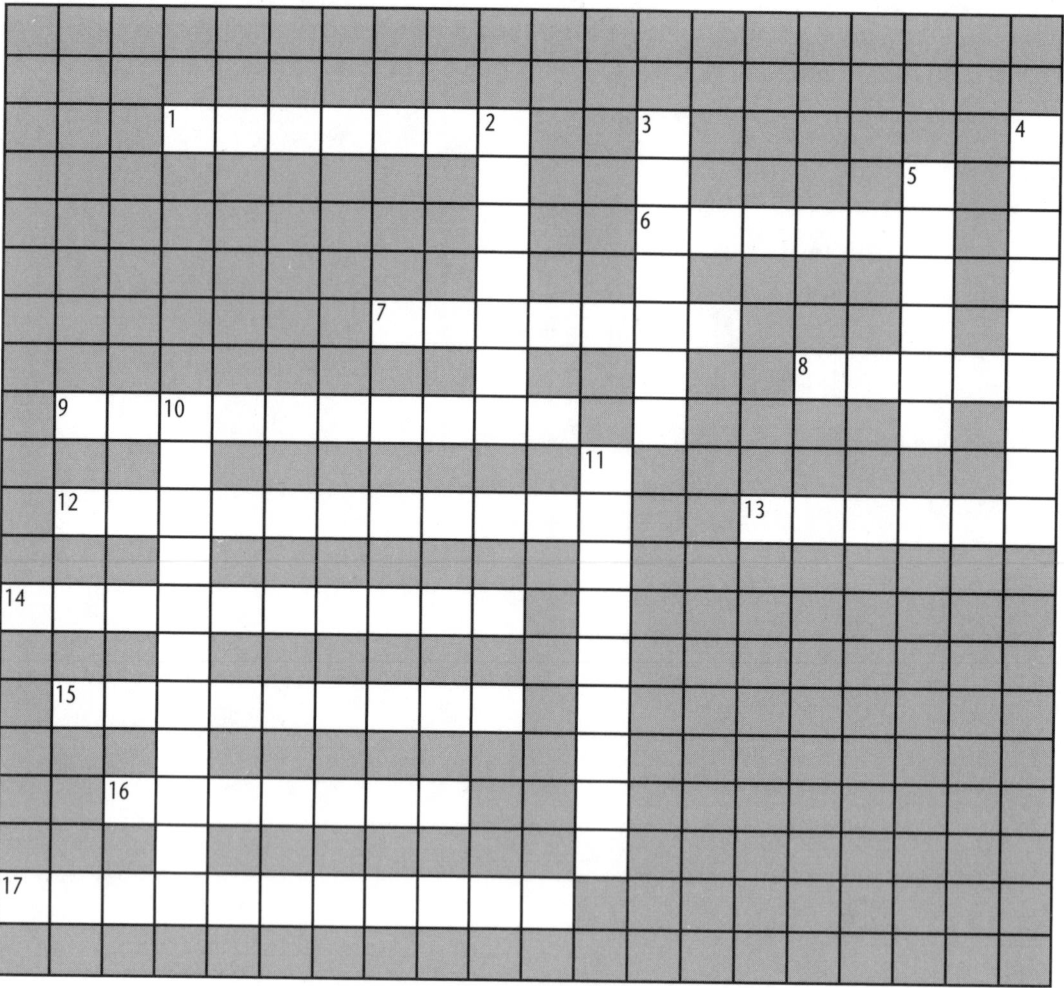


**Across**

1. a shortage of oxygen in the tissues
6. an allergic reaction that blocks the passageways to the lungs
7. one of the two branches leading to the lungs
8. the main organs of the respiratory system
9. the flap of tissue that keeps food out of the windpipe
12. internal or external transferring of oxygen and carbon dioxide
13. a moist membrane covering the lung and chest cavity walls
14. when air is pushed out of the lungs
15. a flat sheet of muscle that provides force for breathing
16. spaces within the bones of the skull
17. smaller branches of the bronchi

**Down**

2. tiny air sacs where the exchange of gases takes place
3. the windpipe
4. a disease that damages the elastic walls of the alveoli
5. the voice box
10. air pulled into the lungs
11. a lung infection caused by viruses, bacteria, or fungi

Name ______________________________ Date ______________

# The Kidneys

To maintain a stable internal environment, the body must eliminate wastes and surplus substances. The kidneys are the organs most essential to these processes.

Write the words that match the descriptions or definitions of terms related to the kidney and liquid excretion.

1. ______________ the process of ridding the body of chemical wastes
2. ______________ a nitrogen-containing waste produced from protein breakdown
3. ______________ one of two organs located in the lower back of humans
4. ______________ a liquid waste produced by the kidneys
5. ______________ tubes leading from the kidneys to the urinary bladder
6. ______________ the tube leading from the bladder to the outside of the body
7. ______________ microscopic units in the kidneys that filter the blood
8. ______________ a ball of capillaries in the nephrons
9. ______________ a double walled structure surrounding the glomerulus
10. ______________ part of the nephron closest to Bowman's capsule
11. ______________ a u-shaped structure in the nephron
12. ______________ connects to a large tube called a collecting tubule
13. ______________ the outer portion of the kidney
14. ______________ the central portion of the kidney
15. ______________ the fluid that accumulates in Bowman's capsule
16. ______________ regulates the reabsorption of water
17. ______________ the production of large volumes of urine
18. ______________ artificial filtering of the blood

**Terms**

antidiuretic hormone
glomerular filtrate
Bowman's capsule
proximal convoluted tubule
hemodialysis
distal convoluted tubule
excretion
urine
glomerulus
cortex
Henle's loop
urethra
medulla
nephrons
urea
kidneys
ureters
diuresis

Name ______________________________ Date ______________

# The Nerves of Us

The nervous system of humans is extremely complicated. Much is known about its structure and function. Answer the questions below.

1. What are the parts of the central nervous system?

2. What structures make up the peripheral nervous system?

3. What is the difference between an involuntary and a voluntary response?

4. What are the major regions of the brain? What do they regulate?

5. What is a neuron? What are its three main components?

6. Explain a threshold stimulus.

7. What two elements are most associated with nerve impulses?

8. What is a synapse?

9. Briefly, how does a nerve impulse begin, and how is it transmitted?

10. What is the difference between an axon and a dendrite?

Name ______________________________ Date ______________

FRANK SCHAFFER'S **BIOLOGY FOR EVERYDAY**

# The Other Control System: Endocrine

The nervous system is one of two human systems of coordination and control. The other is the endocrine system, a number of ductless glands that secrete chemicals, mostly hormones, that control certain body activities after being released into the blood.

The main elements of the endocrine system are listed below. Explain what hormones each produces. State what function they control.

| Gland | Hormone Produced | Control Function |
|---|---|---|
| 1. anterior lobe of pituitary | | |
| 2. posterior lobe of pituitary | | |
| 3. thyroid | | |
| 4. parathyroid | | |
| 5. adrenal medulla | | |
| 6. adrenal cortex | | |
| 7. ovaries | | |
| 8. testes | | |
| 9. islets of Langerhans | | |
| 10. thymus | | |
| 11. pineal | | |

Name ______________________________ Date ______________

# Ecology and the Environment

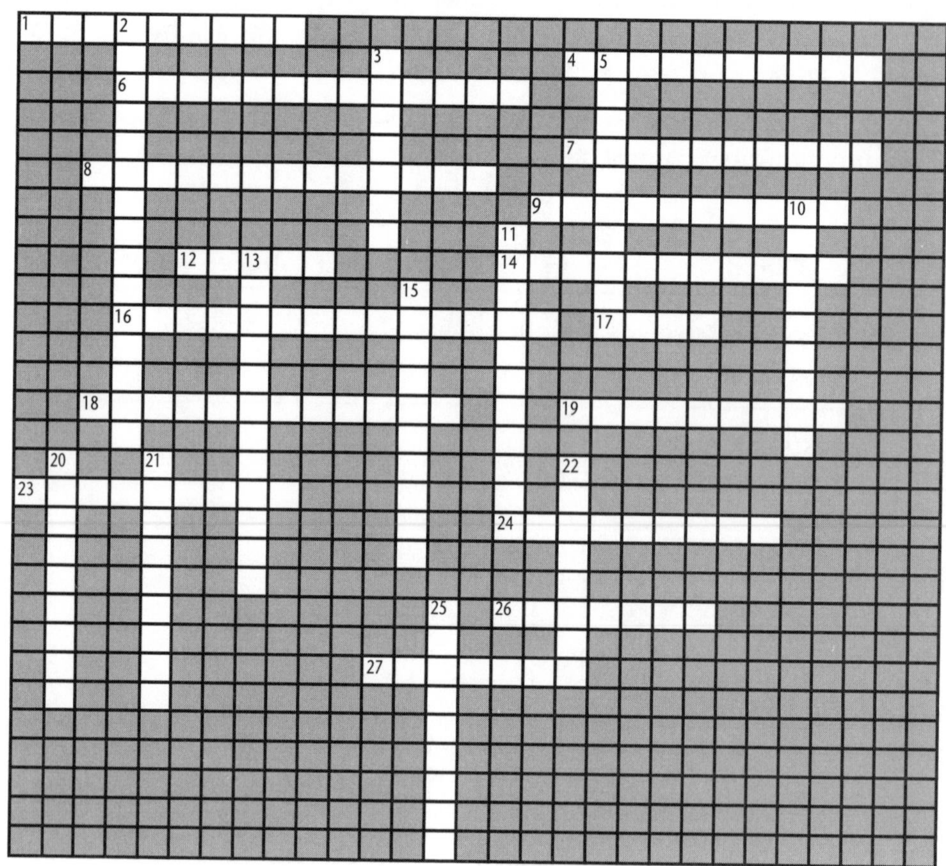

**Across**

1. organisms that make their own food
4. animals that eat other animals
6. ammonia changed by bacteria into compounds containing nitrates
7. a group of same-species organisms living in an ecosystem
8. moisture that falls from clouds
9. animals that eat plants
12. the role of an organism in a community
14. the process of water changing from liquid to vapor
16. amino acids being changed to ammonia
17. a combination of weathered rock, organic matter, water, and gases
18. symbiosis where one organism benefits and the other is not helped or harmed
19. animals that eat plants and animals
23. all the populations of a given area
24. a long-term interaction between two organisms not of the same species
26. the average weather of a place
27. the study of the relationship between living things and the environment

**Down**

2. nitrates changed into nitrogen gas by bacteria
3. a place where an organism lives
5. organisms that make their own food
10. the basic unit of ecology
11. organisms that break down dead organic material
13. water vapor changing to a liquid or ice
15. a symbiotic relationship where one organism benefits and the other is harmed
20. animals that eat other organisms
21. symbiosis where both organisms benefit
22. the amount of moisture in the area
25. the area of the earth where living things exist

Name ______________________ Date ______________

FRANK SCHAFFER'S **BIOLOGY FOR EVERYDAY**

# Biotic Potential: How Much Do You Like Green?

Most living things have a very high potential for population growth. If all the offspring of an organism like a fly survived, all those offspring survived and reproduced at the same rate, and this went on for only a few years, the world would be ankle deep in flies!

Fortunately for the biosphere, there are limiting factors that keep a species from reaching its biotic potential. It's interesting to look at an example. What could happen if...

**Materials:** a green bell pepper, a scalpel or sharp knife, calculator

Procedure: Carefully cut open the bell pepper with a knife and count the number of seeds inside. Use that information to calculate the biotic potential of one bell pepper fruit. To simplify your results, assume only one fruit per plant and the same number of seeds from each plant.

Fill in the blanks:

1. Total number of seeds from your pepper______________
2. 1st year: Number of plants produced if every seed produces a new plant ______________
3. 2nd year: Number of plants produced if every seed produces a new plant ______________
4. 3rd year: Number of plants produced if every seed produces a new plant ______________
5. 4th year: Number of plants produced if every seed produces a new plant ______________

On another sheet of paper, graph the data, starting with one plant at year zero and answer the questions below.

6. Why was a bell pepper chosen for this activity?
7. What are some of the limiting factors that might regulate the bell pepper's growth to keep it from reaching the biotic potential?
8. What is carrying capacity and how is it different for an agricultural crop like a bell pepper than it is for a fly?
9. Do you think there is a carrying capacity for humans? What might be some limiting factors that would influence human population growth?

Name ______________________________ Date ____________

FRANK SCHAFFER'S **BIOLOGY FOR EVERYDAY**

# Endangered Species

Over time, many species of plants and animals have disappeared from the earth. The dinosaurs are but one example. Nowadays, the danger of extinction is facing even more and more living things as humans continue to take over and control the earth's surface and resources.

What are some of the animal species that are now in danger? What can be done to prevent their disappearance forever?

A few examples, like the spotted owl, the manatee, the giant panda, the Mexican gray wolf, and most whales, are well known. There are many more in trouble today.

**Materials needed:** reference materials on animals, especially endangered species

Choose an endangered species of animal. Write a short report about that animal. Answer the following questions in your report.

1. Where is this animal found in nature?

   Add a map to your report.

2. Describe the animal and its natural habitat.

   What does it look like?

   What does it eat?

   What special characteristics or behavior does this animal exhibit that makes it interesting?

   What natural limiting factors affect populations of this animal?

3. Why is this animal endangered?

4. What can humans do to keep this animal from becoming extinct?

5. What impact would protecting this animal have on humans?

Name ______________________________ Date ______________

# Echinoderms

Match the letter of the description or definition in the right column with the correct term in the left column.

| | |
|---|---|
| 1. ____ aboral surface | A. means "spiny skin" |
| 2. ____ brittle stars | B. lies within the body of an animal |
| 3. ____ dipleurula | C. the larva of an echinoderm |
| 4. ____ echinodermata | D. surface opposite the mouth |
| 5. ____ endoskeleton | E. surface containing the mouth |
| 6. ____ oral surface | F. hollow tubes that exchange oxygen and carbon dioxide |
| 7. ____ ring canal | G. a structure that allows water into the water-vascular system |
| 8. ____ sea lilies | H. circular tube-structure that directs water into five radial canals |
| 9. ____ sea urchin | I. responsible for starfish motion |
| 10. ____ sieve plate | J. attached to the sea bottom |
| 11. ____ skin gills | K. the most active and widespread of the echinoderms |
| 12. ____ starfish | L. a spiny echinoderm that may be poisonous |
| 13. ____ tube feet | M. considered pests in oyster beds |

Name ______________________________ Date ______________



# The Most Successful: The Arthropods

The phylum Arthropoda contains more species of animals than any other. It includes lobsters, crabs, ants, bugs, spiders, and centipedes. Insects alone comprise more than 750 thousand known species. Answer the following questions about this enormously successful and varied group.

1. What are the three main characteristics that distinguish the arthropods?

2. What are some of the habitats where arthropods are found?

3. Name and describe some members of the class Arachnida.

4. What are some of the benefits of the chitin exoskeleton arthropods possess?

5. Why are the arthropods such a successful phylum?

6. How is a crayfish similar to a lobster? How is it different?

7. How are centipedes and millipedes similar? How are they different?

8. List the main body parts of most insects.

9. Explain the difference between incomplete metamorphosis and complete metamorphosis.

10. How do arthropods communicate with each other?

Name ______________________ Date ______________

# Designer Insects

**Materials:** drawing paper, colored pencils, insect reference materials

Insects vary greatly in size and appearance, from the smallest ant to the largest beetle or butterfly. They all have certain fundamental body parts that make them members of the class Insecta, the largest group of land-dwelling Arthropods.

The main body parts found in insects are:

| | |
|---|---|
| head | thorax |
| abdomen | three jointed pairs of legs |
| two compound eyes | three simple eyes |
| one pair of antennae | |
| several pairs of mouth parts, including mandibles and maxillae | |

In addition, some insects may have one or two pairs of wings. One pair often serves as a cover for the other, as with the Lady Bird Beetle (ladybug).

Examine photos and drawings of insects in reference sources. Design and color your own insect. Make sure it has each of the parts listed above in the appropriate location.

Your insect may have the head of a honeybee and the wings of a Monarch butterfly, or any combination. When you label the parts on your drawing, state which insect "donated" each part.

Name ____________________ Date ____________

FRANK SCHAFFER'S **BIOLOGY FOR EVERYDAY**

# Behavior and Adaptations in Arthropods

One of the reasons why the Arthropods as a group have been so successful on earth for the past 500 million years is their ability to adapt and develop behavioral traits that aid in their survival.

Describe and explain a behavioral trait or adaptation that has helped each of the following Arthropods increase their chances of survival.

1. Honeybees

2. Ants

3. Butterflies

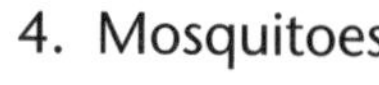

4. Mosquitoes

5. Spiders

6. Termites

Name ______________________________ Date ______________

# Life in a Honeybee Society

The honeybee is only one type of insect that forms colonies and exhibits social behavior. Social organization helps increase the chances of survival by allowing for a division of labor. Some members of the colony are responsible for defense, obtaining food, building nests, and feeding and rearing the young.

Describe the origin, activities and functions in a honeybee hive for the following individuals:

1. queen

2. male

3. female

Name ______________________________ Date ______________

# Invertebrates: Comparing Body Systems

All invertebrates, whether they be sponges or spiders, have the same basic needs and carry out many similar functions. The body parts and systems different invertebrates use to carry out the same functions may be quite different.

Fifteen parts/systems are listed below. Match the letters of the group of invertebrates with the appropriate parts/systems.

**Body Part or System:**

1. ectoderm and endoderm only ________
2. no specialized tissues ________
3. ectoderm, endoderm, and mesoderm ________
4. a true coelom forms ________
5. muscles but no supporting structure ________
6. muscles with a supporting structure ________
7. shells ________
8. endoskeleton ________
9. exoskeleton ________
10. digestive tract with mouth and anus ________
11. no circulatory system ________
12. circulatory system ________
13. nervous system with brain ________
14. asexual or sexual reproduction ________
15. sexual reproduction ________

**Invertebrates:**

A. hydras
B. jellyfish
C. corals
D. sponges
E. flatworms
F. roundworms
G. annelids
H. echinoderms
I. mollusks
J. arthropods

Name ______________________________ Date ______________

# What Are the Chordates?

Animals in the phylum Chordata are the best know to most humans. They have many common characteristics as well as variations. Answer the following questions concerning the chordates.

1. What characteristics place an organism in the phylum Chordata?

2. Name and describe the distinguishing characteristics of the three subphyla of phylum Chordata. Give examples of organisms in each group.

3. Draw and identify an example of each subphyla of phylum Chordata.

Name ______________________________ Date ______________

 FRANK SCHAFFER'S **BIOLOGY FOR EVERYDAY**

# Fish or Frogs?

Fish and amphibians are two vertebrate classes of animals that live in water at least part of their lives. Both are ectotherms (cold-blooded). They obtain most of their body heat from their environment. These two groups have many similarities, but also many differences. Consider fish as a group and one type of amphibian, the frog. How do they match up?

For each characteristic listed below, write "Frog" beside it if the characteristic is common to frogs. Write "Fish" next to it if the characteristic is common to fish. Some characteristics many be common to both classes and some to neither one. A few are common only during certain stages of development, or require a qualified answer like "Frogs during tadpole stage only".

**Characteristics**

1. ______________________ live in water
2. ______________________ breathe with gills
3. ______________________ live on land
4. ______________________ cartilage skeleton
5. ______________________ bony skeleton
6. ______________________ metamorphosis
7. ______________________ fins
8. ______________________ scales
9. ______________________ two-chambered heart
10. ______________________ three-chambered heart
11. ______________________ live in salt water
12. ______________________ have a swim bladder
13. ______________________ breathe with lungs
14. ______________________ have a tail
15. ______________________ reproduce in water
16. ______________________ carnivorous
17. ______________________ endothermic

Name ______________________ Date ______________

# Reptiles

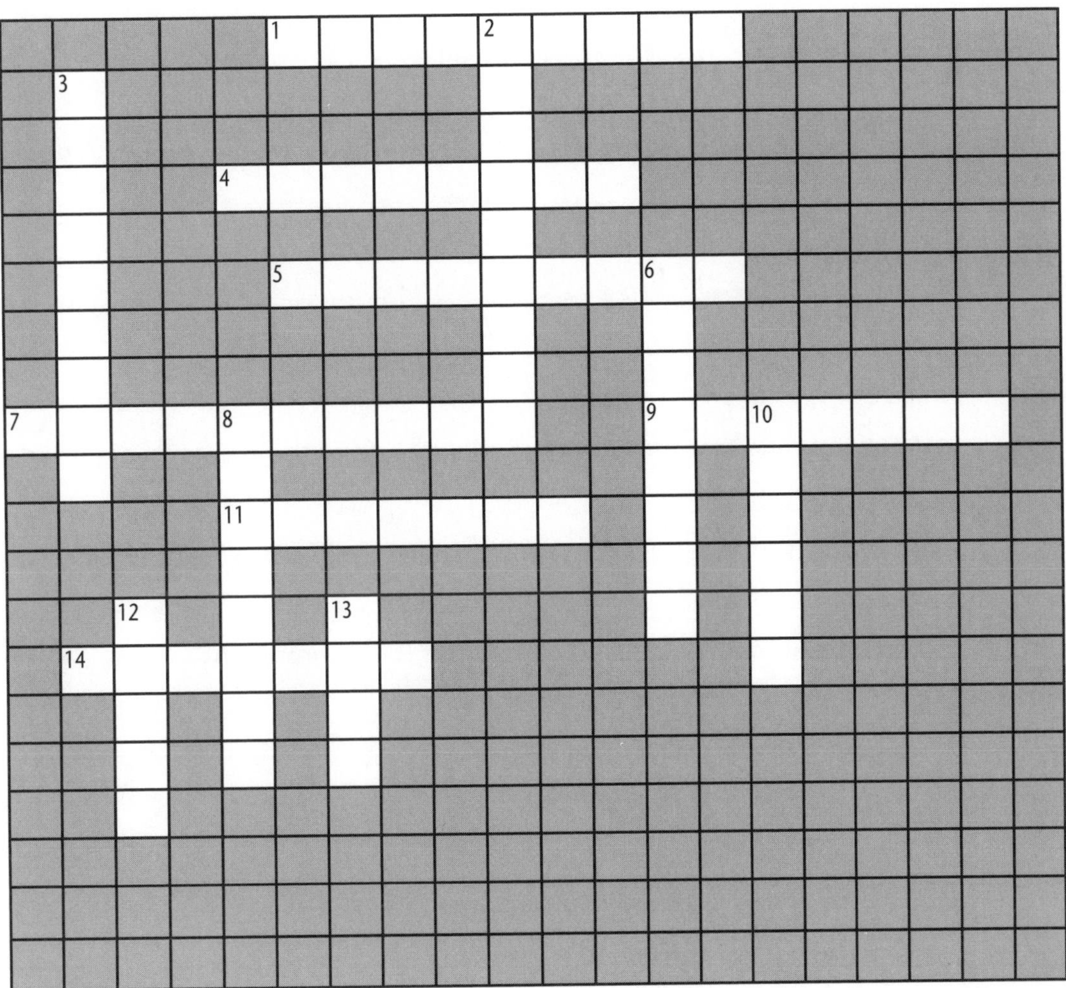


**Across**

1. animals whose embryos develop within eggs inside the body
4. a turtle's dorsal shell
5. an animal that gets its body heat from the environment
7. animals whose embryos develop within the female, then are born alive
9. the only surviving member of a group of reptiles as old as the dinosaurs
11. an egg that has a fluid-filled sac
14. a membrane that grows out from the embryo, lining the inner surface of the shell

**Down**

2. a membrane that forms from the lower end of an embryo's digestive tract
3. a poison that attacks blood cells and vessels
6. ectothermic vertebrates covered with dry, scaly skin
8. a turtle's ventral shield
10. a membrane that grows around the embryo, enclosing it in amniotic fluid
12. a protective covering for the egg
13. a rich source of proteins and lipids for the embryo

Name ______________________________ Date ______________

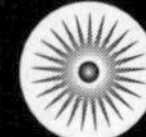

FRANK SCHAFFER'S **BIOLOGY FOR EVERYDAY**

# Reptile Vocabulary Quiz

Write the answers on the lines.

1. ______________ a membrane that grows out from the embryo, lining the inner surface of the shell
2. ______________ ectothermic vertebrates covered with dry, scaly skin
3. ______________ an egg that has a fluid-filled sac
4. ______________ a membrane that forms from the lower end of the embryo's digestive tract
5. ______________ the only surviving member of a group of reptiles as old as the dinosaurs
6. ______________ an animal that gets its body heat from the environment
7. ______________ a poison that attacks blood cells and vessels
8. ______________ the turtle's ventral shield
9. ______________ a protection for the egg
10. ______________ a membrane that grows around the embryo, enclosing it in amniotic fluid
11. ______________ the turtle's dorsal shell
12. ______________ a rich source of proteins and lipids for the embryo
13. ______________ animals whose embryos develop within the female, then are born alive
14. ______________ animals whose embryos develop within eggs inside the body

Name ______________________ Date ____________

# Transport for Plants

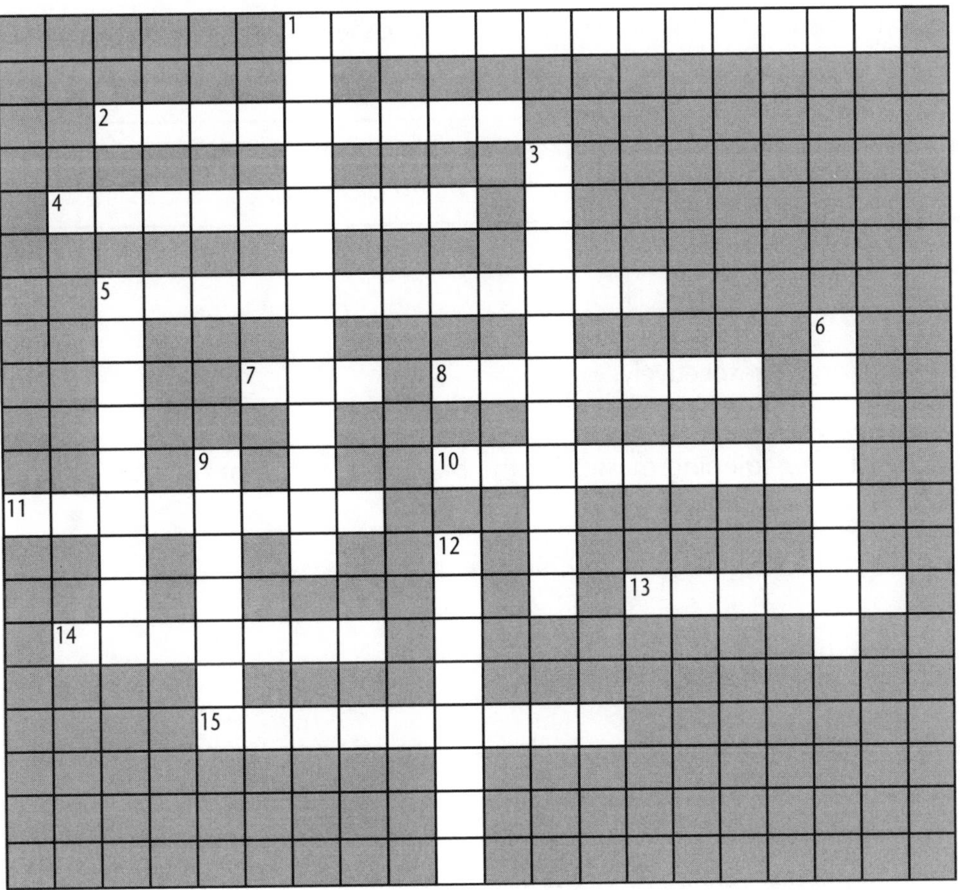


**Across**

1. the escape of water vapor from plant surfaces
2. a process where plants lose excess water through special leaf pores
4. materials dispersing from an area of greater concentration
5. the growth response of plants to moisture
7. the fluid inside phloem tissue
8. loss of turgor in plants due to the lack of water in its tissues
10. a plant that grows where water is scarce
11. the attraction of unlike molecules
13. expanded condition caused by the absorption of water
14. in plants, open ended cells that join end to end to form tubes that conduct materials
15. a plant that stores water in large fleshy stems leaves

**Down**

1. movement of materials within the plant itself
3. the tendency of a liquid to rise in a small diameter tube
5. a plant adapted to growing in salty soils
6. the attraction of like molecules
9. water moving through a selectively permeable membrane
12. a groove cut into a trunk to gain sap from the phloem tubes

Name ______________________ Date ______________

# Measuring Transpiration in Leaves: Part 1

A green plant gives off moisture from its leaves. This is one of the reasons why it is cooler over a forest than cleared ground. In this activity, you will examine one of the variables that affects the transpiration rate.

**Materials:** three clear plastic quart-size resealable bags, a marker that will write on the bags, 30 fresh leaves from a shrub or tree, and a triple beam balance

**Procedure:**

1. Mark the bags 1, 2, and 3 respectively.
2. Measure and record the beginning masses for the bags on Chart A on the next page.
3. Place ten leaves in each bag and seal the opening.
4. Measure and record the mass of each bag on Chart A.
5. Use the difference between the empty and filled bags to calculate the mass of leaves in each bag. Enter that data on your chart.
6. Place bag 1 outside in bright sunlight, bag 2 outside in the shade, and bag 3 inside, out of direct sunlight.
7. After one hour, observe each bag. What's in the bag besides the leaves and air? Carefully remove the leaves, keeping any moisture inside. Reseal the bags.
8. Record the mass of each bag and write the data in the "end mass" section of your chart.
9. Calculate the water loss from the leaves for each bag by subtracting the beginning mass from the ending mass. Enter the answers on the chart in the section "total water loss".
10. Find the percentage of water loss by dividing the water loss by the mass of the leaves in each bag. Enter that data on your chart.

Name ______________________ Date ______________

FRANK SCHAFFER'S **BIOLOGY FOR EVERYDAY**

# Measuring Transpiration in Leaves: Part 2

**Table A**

| **Containers** | **Bag 1** | **Bag 2** | **Bag 3** |
|---|---|---|---|
| Beginning mass of bag | | | |
| Mass of bag with leaves | | | |
| Mass of leaves | | | |
| Ending mass of bag without leaves | | | |
| Total water loss from leaves | | | |
| Percentage water loss | | | |

When you finish the experiment, answer the following questions.

1. Where did the water in the bags come from?

2. Which bag of leaves lost the highest percentage of water? Where was it placed for the hour?

3. What variable do you think was responsible for the difference in percentage water loss?

4. What other variables may have affected this experiment?

5. Why was the percentage of water loss more important in determining the results of this experiment than the total water loss for each bag?

Name ______________________ Date ______________

FRANK SCHAFFER'S **BIOLOGY FOR EVERYDAY**

# Reproduction in Plants

Write the letter of the definition next to the word.

| | |
|---|---|
| 1. ____ petals | A. small leaf-like structures attached to the receptacle of a flower |
| 2. ____ sepal | B. a rounded, thick underground stem that may send up a new plant |
| 3. ____ corm | C. the joining of the twig from one plant to the body of another |
| 4. ____ pistil | D. the long stalk that attaches the anther to the receptacle |
| 5. ____ ovary | E. all the petals |
| 6. ____ seed | F. horizontal stems underground that may form new plants |
| 7. ____ style | G. structures on a conifer that bear the male and female gametophytes |
| 8. ____ cones | H. the upper part of the pistil, where pollen grains land |
| 9. ____ ovules | I. A branch of the parent plant is bent to the ground and covered with dirt. A new plant may form from it. |
| 10. ____ runners | J. the female reproductive structure of the flower |
| 11. ____ layering | K. the reproductive structure of an angiosperm |
| 12. ____ cutting | L. brightly colored structures inside the sepals |
| 13. ____ fruit | M. a structure containing an embryo, food, and a coat |
| 14. ____ anther | N. the structure on the pistil containing the ovules and developing gametophytes |
| 15. ____ stigma | O. the connecting stalk between the stigma and ovary |
| 16. ____ stamens | P. specialized reproductive structures inside a female cone |
| 17. ____ calyx | Q. long horizontal stems or stolons that can form new plants |
| 18. ____ budding | R. grafting a bud instead of a twig to another plant |
| 19. ____ flower | S. a plant part, usually a leaf and stem part, that may form a new plant |
| 20. ____ rhizomes | T. an enlarged, ripened ovary that contains one or more seeds |
| 21. ____ grafting | U. the structure of the stamen where pollen grains are produced |
| 22. ____ filament | V. the male reproductive structures of a flower |
| 23. ____ corolla | W. all the sepals of a flower, together |

Name ______________________________ Date ______________

# Explaining Plant Reproduction

Several processes take place during plant reproduction in both classes of seed-bearing plants: the Gymnosperms and the Angiosperms. The five processes listed below play a role in the reproductive processes of plants. Explain or describe each one of these processes.

1. fertilization

2. germination

3. pollination

4. seed dispersal

5. vegetative propagation

# Factors That Affect Plant Growth

Water, proper temperature, sufficient light, and a growth medium (soil, sand, water) are environmental factors that affect plant growth and development. Below are some chemical compounds that affect plant growth. Write the letters of the answers in the blanks.

1. ____ abscisic acid
2. ____ phytohormones
3. ____ auxins
4. ____ ethylene
5. ____ gibberellins
6. ____ cytokinins

A. a phytohormone that regulates growth
B. a general term for plant hormones
C. a growth inhibitor
D. causes active buds to become dormant
E. promotes growth through cell division
F. causes quick elongation of stems

What other environmental conditions not mentioned above also influence plant growth? On the back of this page, name and describe at least four.

Name ______________________ Date ______________

FRANK SCHAFFER'S **BIOLOGY FOR EVERYDAY**

# Plant Responses and Behavior

Movement of a plant toward or away from a stimulus is called a tropism. Phototropism, geotropism, chemotropism, and thigmotropism are four examples in which a plant or part of a plant grows toward or away from a stimulus. Explain each of these tropisms, and make a sketch of a plant exhibiting each tropism.

1. phototropism

2. geotropism

3. chemotropism

4. thigmotropism

5. Design and describe an experiment you could conduct with a plant demonstrating one of the above tropisms. Write your experiment on another sheet of paper.

6. Using a local variety of tree, tell the life history of that tree from seed through germination, development of shoot, and growth of stem, branches, leaves, and roots. Tell about the production of wood, the development of its flowers, its reproductive phase, and its time of dormancy.

In your life history, include drawings and short text descriptions of what is taking place. Underline important terms. Write your report on another sheet of paper.

Name ______________________ Date ______________



# Charting Simple Invertebrates

Multicelled organisms, called metazoans, can be divided into two groups: Vertebrates (back-boned animals) and Invertebrates (those without backbones). Invertebrates include many phylums. In this activity you will be considering only sponges, coelenterates, and worms. Complete the chart for the listed invertebrates, noting their similarities as well as their differences.

| Organism | Type of symmetry | Digestive system | Nervous system | Feeding mechanism | Where found | Reproduction method |
|---|---|---|---|---|---|---|
| Sponges | | | | | | |
| Hydra | | | | | | |
| Flatworms | | | | | | |
| Flukes | | | | | | |
| Tapeworms | | | | | | |
| Roundworms | | | | | | |
| Earthworms | | | | | | |

Name ______________________________ Date ______________

FRANK SCHAFFER'S **BIOLOGY FOR EVERYDAY**

# Coral Reefs

Corals are simple sea animals of the class Anthozoa that form colonies of polyps. These creatures secrete a non-living calcium carbonate exoskeleton from their epidermis. It is this exoskeleton that we normally see when we look at coral in nature. Over a long period of time, these exoskeletons may form a coral reef, which serves as a habitat for other sea life.

Use outside resources to learn about coral reef formation. Describe the three forms of coral reefs below using text and drawings.

1. Fringing reef:

2. Barrier reef:

3. Atoll:

4. Is there any pattern linking the three types of coral reefs?

5. How are the Guadalupe Mountains of New Mexico related to this activity?

6. Where is the Great Barrier Reef located? Describe it.

# Mollusks

Members of the Phylum Mollusca are soft-bodied invertebrates, with over 50,000 species living today. Characterized by hard external shells, many fossils exist of ancient mollusks that lived in the oceans as long as 600 million years ago.

Listed below are the four classes of mollusks found today. Write several characteristics and examples of each group, then answer the questions.

| | Pelecypoda | Gastropoda | Cephalopoda | Amphineura |
|---|---|---|---|---|
| Class | | | | |
| Characteristics | | | | |
| Examples | | | | |

1. What are some methods of locomotion among mollusks?

2. What are some internal organs of mollusks that are more advanced in development than those in the Annelids?

3. Why are squids so useful in conducting scientific research about learning and animal behavior?

4. What economic benefits do the mollusks provide for humans?

5. What very obvious feature of mollusks is used to classify them into classes?

Name ______________________ Date ______________



# Monerans and Viruses

Answer the questions below using complete sentences.

1. Describe the basic structure of a virus.

2. Why does a virus need a core of nucleic acid to replicate?

3. How is a virus different from a bacteria?

4. Why is so little known about viroids?

5. In what ways are blue-green algae like plants? In what ways are they more like bacteria?

6. Are phages harmful or helpful to humans? Explain your answer.

7. Why are phages the most widely studied of the viruses?

8. What conditions are necessary for most bacteria to grow?

9. In what ways are some bacteria beneficial to humans? Give specific examples.

10. Explain the difference between an obligate aerobe and an obligate anaerobe.

11. How is binary fission different from conjugation?

12. What characteristics identify an organism as belonging to the Kingdom Monera?

Name ______________________________ Date ______________

FRANK SCHAFFER'S **BIOLOGY FOR EVERYDAY**

# The Human Body's Barriers to Infection

The human body has its own defenses against invading pathogens, and is remarkably successful at keeping most disease causing organisms outside the body completely. List nine barriers the human body has to protect against infection. Explain how each barrier carries out its defensive functions.

1.

2.

3.

4.

5.

6.

7.

8.

9.

Name ______________________________ Date ____________

FRANK SCHAFFER'S **BIOLOGY FOR EVERYDAY**

# Diseases and Microbes

Write the letters of the definitions next to the words.

| | |
|---|---|
| 1. ____ vectors | A. identified a procedure for identifying a particular microbe as the cause of a disease |
| 2. ____ host | B. a chemical that helps destroy pathogens and neutralizes their toxins |
| 3. ____ leukocytes | C. the organism on which a parasite lives |
| 4. ____ disease | D. a toxic substance made of a protein, given off by a living bacterium |
| 5. ____ infectious | E. animals that spread diseases but are not affected by them |
| 6. ____ macrophages | F. white blood cells that defend against diseases |
| 7. ____ toxin | G. a condition that interferes with the normal processes of a living thing that has not resulted from an injury |
| 8. ____ epidemic | H. caused by organisms or viruses that enter the body |
| 9. ____ exotoxin | I. phagocytic white blood cells found in the lymph nodes |
| 10. ____ pathogen | J. an organism that causes a disease |
| 11. ____ antibodies | K. a poison released by a pathogen |
| 12. ____ Koch | L. a situation in which a disease is widespread in a population |
| 13. ____ lymph | M. intercellular fluid in special vessels |
| 14. ____ contagious | N. diseases transmitted from one organism to another |
| 15. ____ endotoxin | O. a toxic substance usually given off when the bacterium dies |

Name ______________________________ Date ______________

FRANK SCHAFFER'S **BIOLOGY FOR EVERYDAY**

# Vascular or Non–Vascular Plants?

Vascular plants have specialized tissues for carrying food and water throughout the plant. Non-vascular plants have no such tissues and lack true roots, stems, and leaves.

Place a **V** in the space to the left of the term if it concerns vascular plants and an **NV** if it concerns non-vascular plants. Then define each term.

1. ____ antheridia
2. ____ archegonia
3. ____ capsule
4. ____ club moss
5. ____ fern
6. ____ fiddlehead
7. ____ frond
8. ____ horsetail
9. ____ liverwort
10. ____ moss
11. ____ protonema
12. ____ rhizoid
13. ____ rhizome

Name ______________________________ Date ____________

# Algae: Red, Green, or Brown?

The simplest of the nonvascular plants are the algae. Most algae are aquatic, found in salt or fresh water. A few varieties grow in moist soil and on wood and bark. The three main types of algae are red, green, and brown. Complete the chart below comparing these plants.

| Type | Green Algae | Red Algae | Brown Algae |
|---|---|---|---|
| Where found? | | | |
| Unicellular, colonies, or multicellular? | | | |
| How they reproduce | | | |
| Characteristics | | | |
| Examples | | | |

1. Why can red algae grow at greater depths than green or brown?

2. What commercial uses are there for algae?

Name ______________________ Date ______________

FRANK SCHAFFER'S **BIOLOGY FOR EVERYDAY**

# Seed Plants

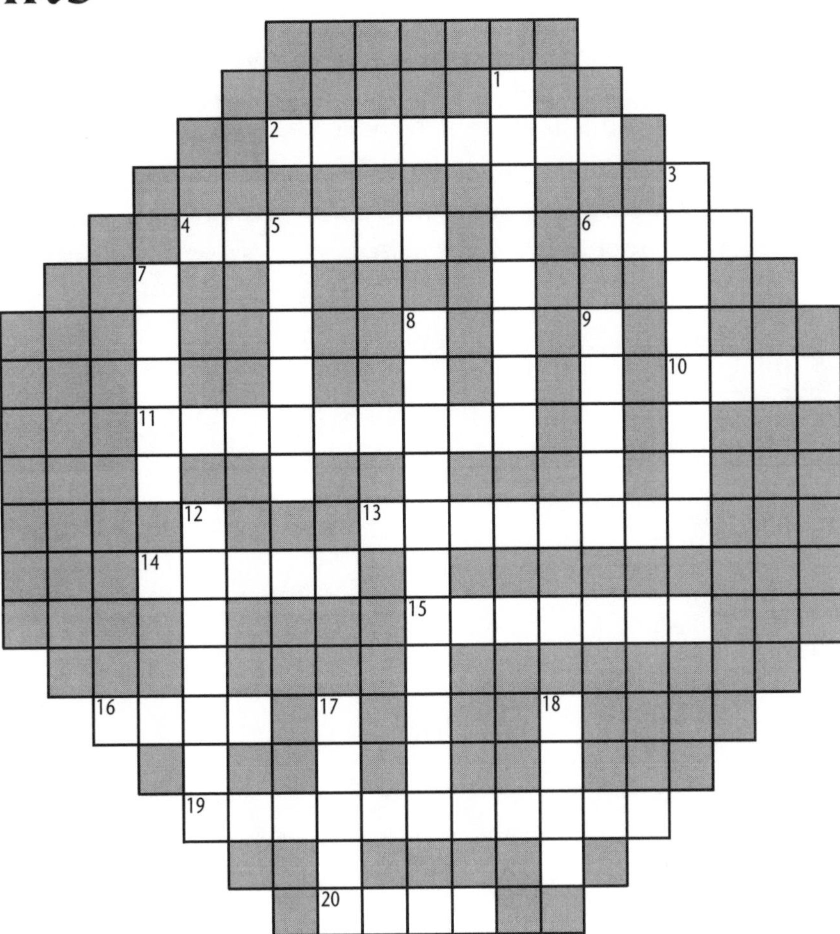

**Across**

2. a pattern made by veins in leaves
4. angiosperms in which each seed contains two primary leaves
6. the organ in a plant that anchors it to the ground
10. tissue made of thick cells, forming the outer protective tissue of woody plants
11. layer of cells that covers the entire plant
13. group of plants that usually produce cones or have seeds on their branches
14. the vascular cylinder of a root
15. the stalk connecting the leaf to the stem
16. the plant organ that absorbs sunlight and carries on photosynthesis
19. plants whose seeds develop within ovaries (flowering plants)
20. the structure that conducts water and minerals absorbed by the roots into the leaves

**Down**

1. trees with small fan-shaped leaves
3. angiosperms with each seed containing one primary leaf
5. relative of ancient plants common in the Mesozoic
7. an underground stem adapted for food storage
8. plants whose seeds do not develop within ovaries (some bear cones)
9. the broad, flat part of a leaf
12. openings in the leaf that allow water and oxygen to pass out, and carbon dioxide to enter
17. vascular bundles in a leaf
18. the outermost layer of protective tissue produced by the stem

Name ______________________ Date ______________

# Getting to the Root of Green Plants

The underground organ of most seed plants, the root, anchors the plant to the ground or other surface. This organ also absorbs water and minerals from the soil and conducts these materials to the above-ground portions of the plant. Sometimes food manufactured in the leaves is stored in the roots.

Use textbook references as guides. Make clear, quality sketches of both a longitudinal section and cross section of a typical root, labeling the following structures: cortex, endodermis, epidermis, meristematic region, pericycle, phloem, root cap, root hair, stele, xylem.

1. How have roots adapted to special environments like swamps?

2. What purpose do the nodules on roots of alfalfa and clover serve?

Name ______________________________ Date ____________

# Learning Leaves

**Materials:** textbook references of leaf internal structure, leaves from three different types of plants

The greatest amount of photosynthesis takes place in the leaf of a plant. The leaf also releases water to the atmosphere. Use textbook references to make a detailed, quality drawing of the internal structure of a leaf. Include and label the following structures: epidermis, intercellular space, palisade mesophyll, phloem, spongy mesophyll, stoma, and xylem.

Sketch and label the parts of three different plant leaves your teacher has supplied. Label the following structures: blade, veins, midrib, and petiole.

1. What function do the stomata of leaves serve?

2. How have leaves adapted to differing environmental conditions?

Name ______________________ Date ______________

FRANK SCHAFFER'S **BIOLOGY FOR EVERYDAY**

# Stem Studies

The stem of a plant is the structure that usually extends above the roots and provides a structural network for the leaves and other parts of the plant that it produces, like flowers. Stems conduct water and minerals upward and food down to the roots.

**Materials:** twigs from three different woody dicot plants, like elm, cottonwood, beech, oak, poplar, etc.

1. Make three sketches of twigs from three different woody dicot plants. Identify and label the following structures on each: bundle scar, internode, lateral bud, leaf scar, lenticel, node, terminal bud, and terminal bud scar.

2. What differences allow you to determine which twig belongs to which plant?

3. How have stems adapted to environmental conditions?

4. What is the function of the xylem and phloem in stems?

Name ______________________________ Date ______________

FRANK SCHAFFER'S **BIOLOGY FOR EVERYDAY**

# Plant Transportation Systems

Plants depend on several processes for taking in the materials they need from the environment and eliminating waste products. They also need to move materials and food within their leaves, stems, and roots.

Explain or describe the following plant transportation systems, naming the materials transported by each.

1. osmosis

2. active transport

3. diffusion

4. root pressure

5. capillary action

6. transpiration (pull or lift)

Name ______________________________ Date ______________



# Really Ancient History

Write the letters of the descriptions or definitions in the blanks.

| | |
|---|---|
| 1. ____ adaptive radiation | A. the solution that made up the early oceans |
| 2. ____ australopithecines | B. a mound of limestone formed by ancient one-celled organisms |
| 3. ____ convergence | C. may have resulted in the creation of eukaryotic cells |
| 4. ____ Cro-Magnons | D. largest interval of geologic time |
| 5. ____ divergence | E. small period of geologic time |
| 6. ____ epoch | F. sudden disappearance of many species |
| 7. ____ era | G. results in the rapid evolution of many species |
| 8. ____ hominid | H. distant relatives of insects |
| 9. ____ homo habilis | I. one theory of mass extinction |
| 10. ____ mass extinction | J. increase in differences among descendants of a species |
| 11. ____ meteorite impact hypothesis | K. increase of similarities among different species |
| 12. ____ Neanderthals | L. human-like or human species |
| 13. ____ primordial soup | M. believed to be the first hominids |
| 14. ____ stromatolite | N. the first members of their genus |
| 15. ____ symbiotic hypothesis | O. became extinct about 35,000 years ago |
| 16. ____ trilobite | P. the first modern humans |

Name ______________________________ Date ______________

# A "Buggy" Classification Key

To use an insect identification key, look at the bug to be identified. Start with the first question. Question 1 might say, "Does the bug have antennae?" If the answer is yes, go to Question 2. If no, go to Question 3. Each question will be about the presence or absence of another feature.

Eight imaginary bugs are drawn below. Design a classification key that will identity each one and only that one. Each question on your key should be a yes-or-no question about the presence or absence of an observed physical feature, like wings, spots, antennae, eyes, claws, and so on.

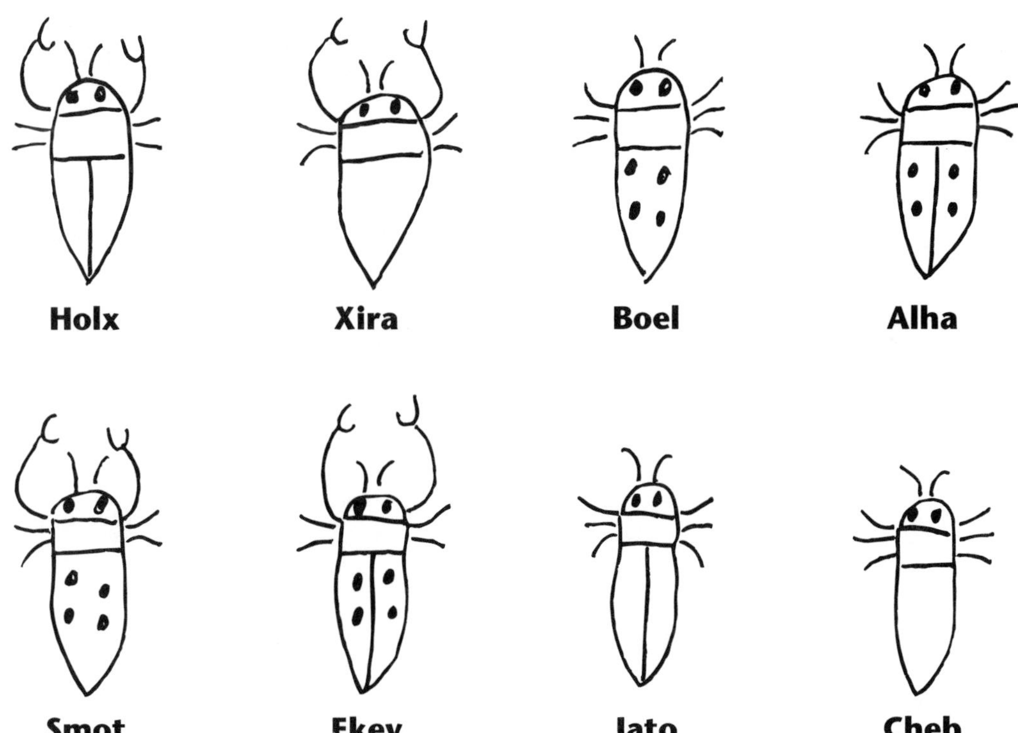

Name ______________________________ Date ______________

FRANK SCHAFFER'S **BIOLOGY FOR EVERYDAY**

# Finding Common and Scientific Names

**Materials:** This paper, dictionaries, field guides or reference books on wildlife. Also local extension agents, forestry officers, and nurseries are good sources.

Learn the common names (there may be more than one) and the scientific names for 15 plants and 15 animals found in your area. List them below. If the common names and/or the scientific name is also descriptive of that organism, indicate what the description is.

> Example: Lepus americanus (scientific name), the snowshoe hare (common name). The hare gets its common name from the dense hair pads it develops on its feet in winter, which allow it to walk on the snow. Another common name is the varying hare because it changes its coat from brown to white as a winter adaptation.

What does *americanus* in the scientific name tell you?

**Your list of 15 local plants and 15 animals:**

| Scientific name | Common names | Description (from names) |
|---|---|---|
| | | |

Name ____________________ Date ____________

# Viruses and Monerans

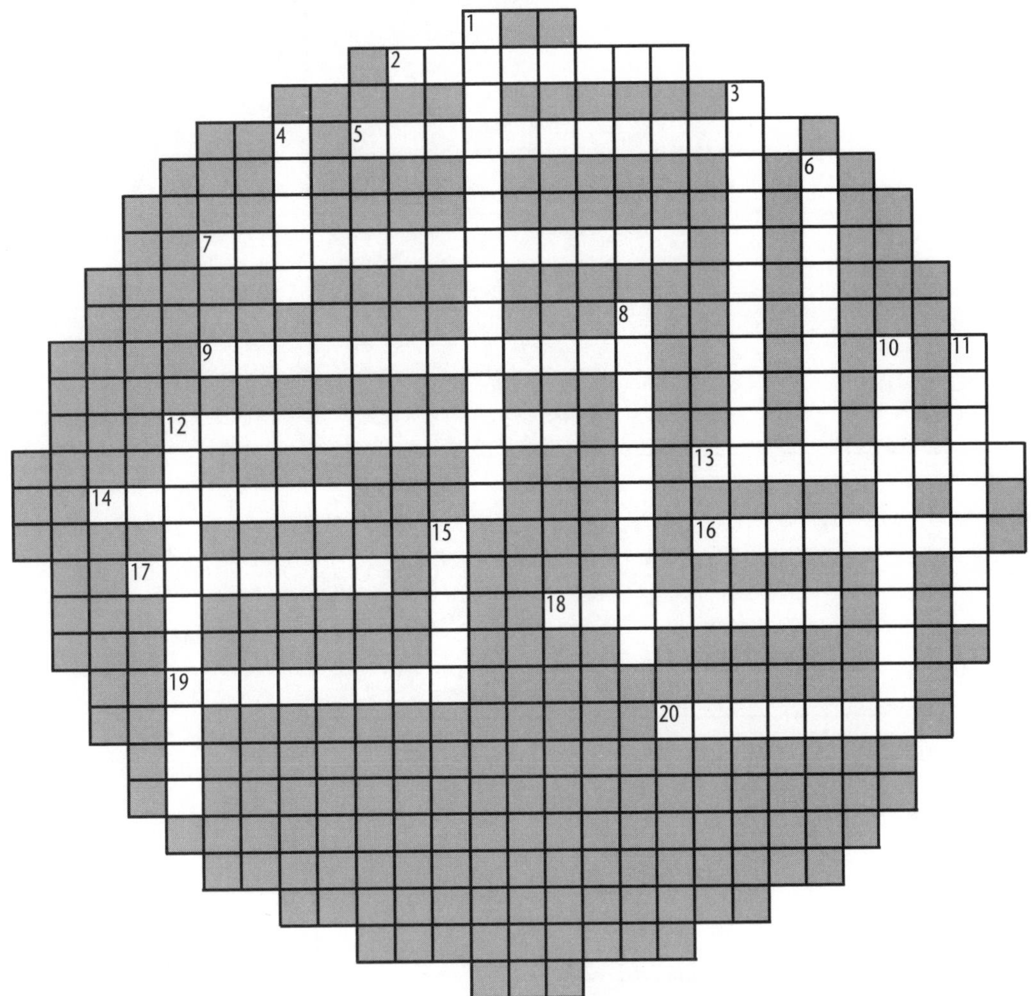

**Across**

2. organisms that live in or feed on a host organism, causing harm to the host
5. the transfer of host DNA to another organism by a virus
7. a virus that infects bacteria
9. the protein shell and nucleic acid of a virus
12. the reproduction of a virus
13. obligate bacteria that grow only in the absence of oxygen
14. rod shaped bacteria
16. spiral shaped bacteria
17. obligate bacteria that require oxygen
18. viral DNA attached to a bacterial chromosome
19. organisms that use dead organic matter as food
20. naked RNA that invades a cell

**Down**

1. genetic material absorbed from the environment replaces part of a bacterium's DNA
3. transferring genetic material by direct cell-to-cell contact
4. spherical shaped bacteria
6. a spore that forms within a cell
8. when a phage sticks to the surface of a bacterial cell
10. tiny monerans without cell walls
11. the kingdom that includes prokaryotes (bacteria)
12. bacteria-like organisms that cannot live outside living tissue
15. a submicroscopic particle made of a nucleic acid and protein

Name ____________________ Date ____________



# Classifying Viruses

Below is a chart listing common viruses. Complete the chart. Then answer the questions.

| Name | Host | Capsid shape | Envelope | Nucleic acid | Size |
|---|---|---|---|---|---|
| 1. bacterial viruses | | | | | |
| 2. chicken pox virus | | | | | |
| 3. cold virus | | | | | |
| 4. flu virus | | | | | |
| 5. herpes virus | | | | | |
| 6. polio virus | | | | | |
| 7. smallpox virus | | | | | |
| 8. tobacco mosaic virus | | | | | |
| 9. yellow fever virus | | | | | |

10. Which viruses are sometimes called phages?

11. Which of the above viruses are often associated with seasons?

12. Which of the viruses listed can infect humans?

13. Which of the viruses infecting humans have vaccines been developed to counter?

14. Make a ten-centimeter-tall drawing of a virus on the back of this paper, labeling the structures present.

Name ______________________________ Date ______________

**FRANK SCHAFFER'S BIOLOGY FOR EVERYDAY**

# Classifying Bacteria by Shape

Several examples of common bacteria are drawn below. Circle the names of those that are round shaped. Underline those that are rod shaped. Those that remain will be considered spiral shaped.

Find which disease or food is associated with each bacteria. Write the answer on the line by each illustration.

Diplococcus meningitidis
1. ______________

Streptococcus pyogenes
2. ______________

Bacillus tetani
3. ______________

Bacillus botulinum
4. ______________

Diplococcus pneumoniae
5. ______________

Staphylococcus aureus
6. ______________

Treponema pallidum
7. ______________

Bacillus anthracis
8. ______________

Streptococcus lactis
9. ______________

Bacillus typhosa
10. ______________

Bacillus lactis
11. ______________

Write the name of the bacteria that best matches the description in the blank.

12. ______________ general shape: rod, found in pairs
13. ______________ general shape: rod, found single, bulge at end
14. ______________ general shape: round, found in chains, large
15. ______________ general shape: rod, single, with flagella
16. ______________ general shape: round, found in clumps
17. ______________ general shape: round found in chains, small
18. ______________ general shape: round, in pairs, no heavy cover
19. ______________ general shape: spiral
20. ______________ general shape: rod, found in chains
21. ______________ general shape: round, found in pairs, heavy cover
22. ______________ general shape: rod, bulge in middle

Name ______________________________ Date ______________



# Searching for Protists

Use the definitions below to find the words hidden in the puzzle. Circle the words and write them on the appropriate lines.

| C | D | Y | E | B | D | S | T | O | P | S | E | Y | E | I |
|---|---|---|---|---|---|---|---|---|---|---|---|---|---|---|
| L | E | E | U | G | L | E | N | A | M | T | N | K | I | L |
| S | L | D | R | P | T | Z | A | U | A | O | U | T | E | A |
| N | C | F | O | R | A | M | I | N | I | F | E | R | A | M |
| A | I | R | U | M | O | C | R | T | D | L | C | I | S | S |
| O | L | H | K | E | E | H | A | G | O | A | T | C | N | A |
| Z | L | K | B | M | N | G | L | U | P | G | O | H | A | L |
| O | E | A | A | E | U | W | O | L | O | E | P | O | O | P |
| R | P | R | Y | J | Y | C | I | L | D | L | L | C | Z | O |
| O | A | J | N | M | M | C | D | E | U | L | A | Y | O | D |
| P | Y | O | C | I | L | I | A | T | E | A | S | S | T | N |
| S | C | U | V | R | O | Z | R | Y | S | T | M | T | O | E |
| E | U | G | L | E | N | O | I | D | P | E | L | S | R | Y |
| M | O | N | A | M | U | I | D | O | M | S | A | L | P | R |
| X | D | I | A | T | O | M | S | T | S | I | T | O | R | P |

1. ______________ kingdom made of simple eukaryotic organisms
2. ______________ animal-like protists
3. ______________ an organism with both plant and animal traits
4. ______________ a group of about 800 algal protist species
5. ______________ a red, light-sensitive structure on a euglena
6. ______________ algal protists that live within a two-part shell
7. ______________ a mass of cytoplasm that contains many nuclei
8. ______________ means "false feet"
9. ______________ a sarcodine with a lacy, glassy shell of silica
10. ______________ group of sarcodines with shells of calcium carbonate
11. ______________ a freshwater sarcodine, moves using pseudopodia
12. ______________ the clear, outer layer of an amoeba's cytoplasm
13. ______________ the granular cytoplasm containing an amoeba's organelles
14. ______________ a protective shell that forms around a protozoan cell, providing protection from harsh conditions
15. ______________ one-celled organisms with many cilia
16. ______________ a ciliate often found in fresh water, resembling a slipper
17. ______________ the firm, flexible outer covering of a paramecium
18. ______________ the funnel-like tube leading to the mouth of a paramecium
19. ______________ kind of sexual reproduction in paramecia
20. ______________ sharp pointed structures used by a paramecium for defense or catching prey
21. ______________ parasitic protozoans that form small cells called spores during their life cycle
22. ______________ a group of animal-like protists that have flagella

Name ____________________ Date ____________



# The Three Subkingdoms of Protista

Complete the chart comparing the three subkingdoms of the Kingdom Protista.

| Subkingdoms | | Phylums | Example organisms | Characteristics |
|---|---|---|---|---|
| **Gymnomycota** fungal protists | 1. | | | |
| **Protophyta** algal protists | 2. | | | |
| | 3. | | | |
| | 4. | | | |
| **Protozoa** the animal-like protists | 5. | | | |
| | 6. | | | |
| | 7. | | | |
| | 8. | | | |

Name ________________________________ Date ____________

FRANK SCHAFFER'S **BIOLOGY FOR EVERYDAY**

# There's a Fungus Among Us

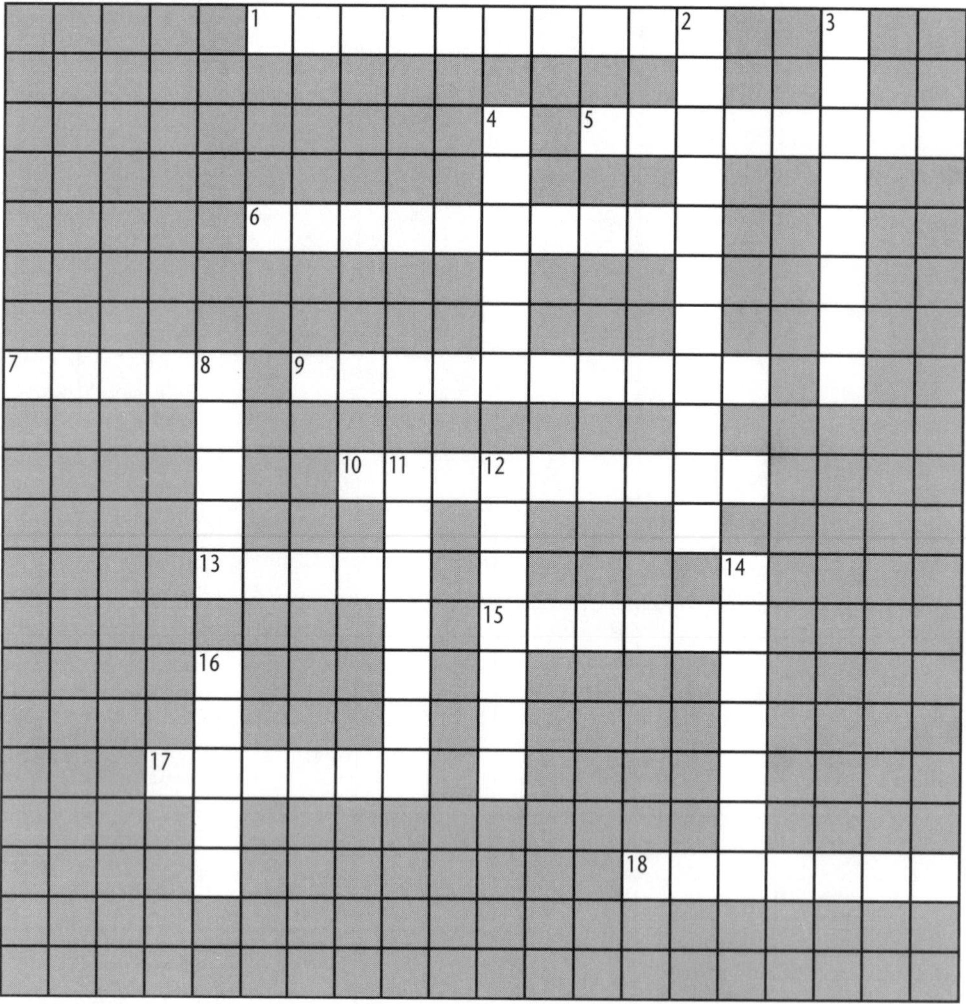

**Across**

1. a structure formed by the association of a fungus and plant roots
5. a network of fungal hyphae
6. a spore case
7. the part of a mushroom where the spores are formed
9. thick-walled diploid spores
10. spore with two flagella
13. a spore sac
15. a symbiotic association between a fungus and a bacterium, protist, or green algae
17. branching filaments or tubes that make up most fungi
18. a club-shaped spore structure

**Down**

2. yeast and bread mold are in this phylum
3. small, branching hyphae growing downward from the stolon
4. an organism made of eukaryotic cells with cell walls; feeds by absorbing organic substances
8. cross walls in hyphae
11. the fertilized egg of an oomycete
12. hyphae that are parallel to the fungus' growth medium
14. draws the edge of the mushroom cap toward the stem
16. the stem of a mushroom

Name ______________________ Date ______________

FRANK SCHAFFER'S **BIOLOGY FOR EVERYDAY**

# Cell Reproduction

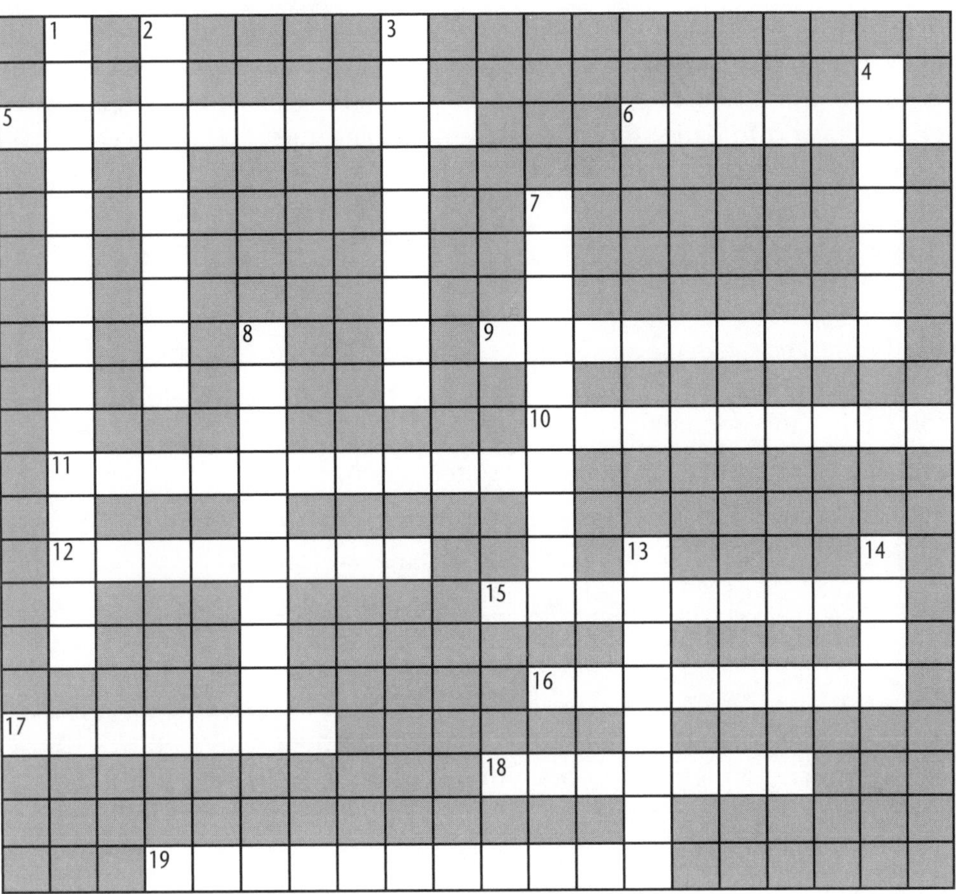


**Across**

5. connects each pair of chromatids
6. cell division where the chromosome number is reduced by half and gametes are formed
9. half the number of chromosomes
10. the formation of gametes in females
11. units that form DNA molecules
12. the pairing of homologs in prophase I
15. the chromosomes again become threadlike, a nuclear membrane forms around each mass of chromatin
16. the chromosome material condenses and appears as shortened, distinct rods
17. specialized cells that join during sexual reproduction
18. cell division where each daughter cell receives the same number of chromosomes as the parent cell
19. the division of the cytoplasm into two sections

**Down**

1. the formation of sperm cells
2. the paired chromatids move to the center of the cell, each attached to a spindle fiber
3. one of two distinct strands making up a chromosome
4. the total number of chromosomes in a cell that contains chromosomes in homologous pairs
7. structure carrying the information needed to control cell activities
8. the period in which cells carry out non-mitosis activities
13. chromosomes that carry the same kinds of genetic information, in the same order
14. a segment of DNA that codes for a particular protein

Name ______________________________ Date ______________

FRANK SCHAFFER'S **BIOLOGY FOR EVERYDAY**

# DNA Replication and Protein Synthesis

A short segment of DNA that contains a chemical message coding for the development of a certain trait is called a gene. A DNA molecule is composed of two chains of nucleotides joined by weak hydrogen bonds. Nucleotides consist of a phosphate group, a sugar called deoxyribose, and a nitrogenous base. For genetic information to be passed along to daughter cells, DNA molecules must be copied identically. This process is called DNA replication.

1. Four steps of DNA replication are summarized below. Number the steps in the correct order.

    ____ Each half of the DNA molecule serves as a template or pattern for the formation of a new half. Bases in free nucleotides join with the correct bases on the two exposed chains. Cytosine always bonds to guanine and adenine always bonds to thymine.

    ____ The two new molecules of DNA become twisted again, taking on the form of a double helix.

    ____ Bonds form between the sugars and phosphates of the newly paired nucleotides on the DNA chains. Two identical copies of the original molecule are formed.

    ____ The double helix untwists and the bonds between the bases of the DNA molecule are broken. The two chains of nucleotides separate from one end down, like a zipper being opened.

2. The process of transcription results in the formation of messenger RNA (mRNA). Messenger RNA carries the instructions for making a particular protein from the DNA in the nucleus to the ribosomes of a cell. Summarize transcription in three steps.

3. Translation is the construction of a protein molecule using the code provided by mRNA within the ribosomes. Explain translation in five or six steps.

Name ______________________________ Date ______________

# Comparing Mitosis and Meiosis

The two processes of cell division (mitosis and meiosis) have many features in common, but they are very important events that are quite different. Listed below are fourteen statements concerning mitosis or meiosis. In each blank, indicate which of the two types of cell division is best described.

1. ________ No pairing of homologs takes place
2. ________ Produces two daughter cells
3. ________ Takes place with one celled organisms
4. ________ Forms gametes in eukaryotic cells
5. ________ The chromosome number is reduced by half
6. ________ Forms egg or sperm cells
7. ________ Occurs in most types of eukaryotic cells
8. ________ Maintains the chromosome number
9. ________ Homologous chromosomes are paired
10. ________ Two divisions take place
11. ________ Four daughter cells are produced
12. ________ Daughter cells are identical to parent cell
13. ________ Daughter cells are different from each other and from parent cell
14. ________ One division takes place
15. What two events determine the number of chromosomes that make the outcome of mitosis and meiosis so different?
16. Describe the embryo resulting from sexual reproduction if meiosis resulted in the same number of chromosomes as with mitosis.
17. Why is crossing over important in sexually reproducing organisms?

# Answer Key

**CHARACTERISTICS OF LIVING THINGS, page 1**

Examples will vary.

1. produce new organisms like themselves
2. obtaining and using food
3. react to changes in surroundings
4. a single cell is the smallest unit of living things
5. releasing energy from food
6. fitted to live in a particular environment
7. takes in food, gases and/or other materials
8. increases in size and goes through a life cycle
9. able to change location, position, or orientation
10. releases waste materials
11. manufactures needed substances
12. controls body processes as circumstances change

**COMMUNICATION IN BIOLOGY, page 2**

**1.** A, **2.** G, **3.** H, **4.** B, **5.** O, **6.** C, **7.** P, **8.** T, **9.** N, **10.** S, **11.** I, **12.** J, **13.** M, **14.** R, **15.** L, **16.** F, **17.** Q, **18.** E, **19.** K, **20.** D

**MEASURING LENGTHS METRICALLY, page 3**

**1.** 38mm; 3.8cm, **2.** 31mm; 3.1cm, **3.** 64mm; or 6.4cm, **4.** 115mm; 11.5cm, **5.** 51mm; 5.1cm, **6.** 84mm; 8.4cm, **7.** 105mm; 10.5cm, **8.** 140mm; 14.0cm, **9.** 18mm; 1.8cm, **10.** 41mm; 4.1cm, **11.** 79mm; 7.9cm, **12.** 135mm; 13.5cm, **13.** 125mm; 12.5cm, **14.** 10mm; 1.0cm, **15.** 158mm; 15.8cm, **16-25.** Variable

**THE CHEMISTRY OF BIOLOGY, page 4**

| ACROSS | DOWN |
|---|---|
| 1. MOLECULE | 1. MONOSACCHARIDE |
| 2. MIXTURE | 3. ISOTOPE |
| 4. ORGANIC | 5. ATOM |
| 7. SUSPENSION | 6. ISOMER |
| 8. CARBOHYDRATE | 9. BASE |
| 13. ION | 10. LIPIDS |
| 14. COLLOID | 11. ELEMENT |
| 15. SOLUTE | 12. PROTEINS |
| 16. DISACCHARIDES | 17. COMPOUND |
| 19. PRODUCTS | 18. ACID |

**FORMING ORGANIC BONDS, page 5**

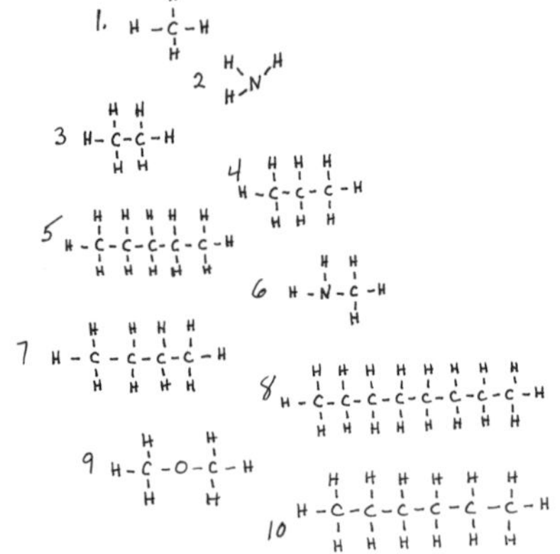

**CELL STRUCTURE AND FUNCTION, page 6**

| ACROSS | DOWN | |
|---|---|---|
| 2. CHROMOSOME | 1. CHLOROPLAST | 10. NUCLEOLUS |
| 9. MITOCHONDRIA | 3. EUKARYOTES | 11. CHROMATIN |
| 13. CYTOPLASM | 4. CILIA | 12. PROKARYOTES |
| 15. CELL | 5. CHROMOPLAST | 14. ORGANELLES |
| 16. FLAGELLUM | 6. VACUOLES | 18. LYSOSOMES |
| 17. MICROFILAMENTS | 7. MICROTUBULES | 19. NUCLEUS |
| 20. PROTOPLASM | 8. RIBOSOMES | |

**COMPARING CELLS, page 7**

**Bacteria**

1. cytoplasm: gel-like material within the cell
2. ribosome: synthesizes proteins

**Plants**

3. above structure and functions, plus
4. cell membrane: structure that helps regulate passage of materials in and out of the cell
5. nucleus: control center of cell
6. nucleolus: synthesizes and stores RNA
7. mitochondrion: cell powerhouse, releases energy for cell functions
8. endoplasmic reticulum: passageways for movement of materials within the cell
9. nuclear membrane: regulates flow of materials in and out of nucleus
10. Golgi apparatus: prepares materials for secretion within the cell
11. vacuole: fluid-filled structure that stores materials lysosome: contains digestive enzymes, digests foreign particles
12. microfilaments: thread-like fibers that produce a flowing motion
13. microtubules: help give shape to cells chloroplasts: site of food making process in plants
14. leucoplasts: storage plastids
15. chromoplasts: plastids that contain red, yellow, or orange pigments

**Animals:** All the above structures except cell wall and plastids.

16. Also, vacuoles are usually small.

**BASIC CHEMISTRY IN LIVING CELLS, page 8**

**1.** K, **2.** C, **3.** A, **4.** D, **5.** H, **6.** E, **7.** L, **8.** I, **9.** G, **10.** N, **11.** B, **12.** F, **13.** O, **14.** M, **15.** J

**FACTORS AFFECTING PHOTOSYNTHESIS: PART 1, page 9**

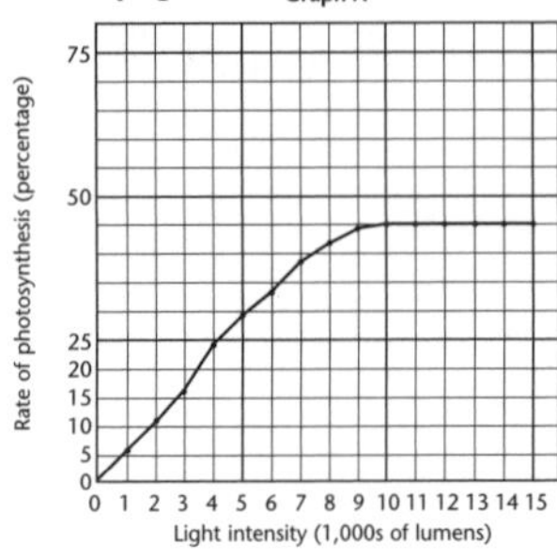


1. After 10,000, the rate levels off.
2. Perhaps other factors, like enzyme action are more important above 10,000 lumens.

**FACTORS AFFECTING PHOTOSYNTHESIS: PART 2, page 10**

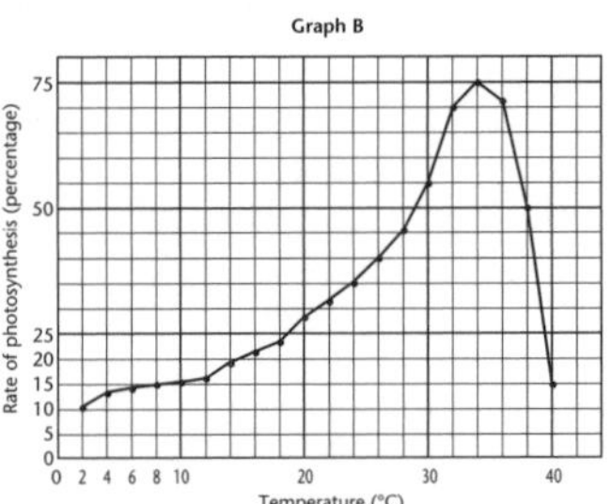


1. Graph A shows the rate of photosynthesis increasing at a rapid, steady rate, then leveling off at around 9,000–10,000 lumens. In Graph B, the rate increases slowly until the temperature reaches 20°C, then more rapidly, peaking at around 34°. Above that temperature, the rate drops off sharply.
2. The shape of Graph B indicates there is a small optimum temperature range and a maximum temperature limit.
3. Above 34%, the rate of photosynthesis quickly drops toward zero.
4. Maybe the heat denatures the protein.

**COMPARING EARTH'S BIOMES, page 11**

**Average rainfall:** less than 25 cm; 35 to 75 cm; 75 to 125 cm; more than 200 cm; 25 to 75 cm less than 25cm

**Average temperature:** –26°C to 4°C; –10°C to 14°C; 6°C to 28°C; 25°C to 27°C; 0°C to 25°C; 24°C to 32°C

**Location:** northern N.A., Asia, Europe, Greenland, many small islands; much of N.A., Europe, Asia, taiga of Russia; south of coniferous forest, New Zealand, Tasmania, east coast of Australia, parts of China, Japan; Amazon basin, west and central Africa, many Pacific islands; N.A. prairie, S.A. pampas, Asia steppes, Africa veldt; N.A. west, Sahara, Gobi

**Typical plants:** lichens, mosses, flowering plants-herbs, dwarf shrubs; pines, spruce, hemlocks, firs; maples, birches, oaks, shrubs, ferns; more plants than any other biome, many trees, vines, less ground plants; grasses, few trees; grasses, shrubs, cacti

**Typical animals:** caribou, wolves, musk ox, lemmings, ducks, geese; lynxes, bears, moose, elk, hares, squirrels; many birds, mice, shrews, snails, rabbits, deer, foxes, owls; many tree dwelling animals, bats, monkeys, sloths, birds, armadillos, jaguars, anteaters, tigers, many insects; herds of buffalo, antelope, zebras, giraffes, lions, rabbits, prairie dogs; rodents, deer, antelope, rabbits, lizards, snakes, birds

**Other features:** growing season of 60 days, permafrost, no trees, no southern tundra; great source of timber; man has developed this biome extensively, much cut down; fragile ecosystem with poor soil, recovers very slowly from deforestation; much cultivated due to good, deep soil; can be hot or cold deserts

**ARE YOU A BIRD-BRAIN?, page 12**

**1.** N, **2.** D, **3.** E, **4.** A, **5.** H, **6.** O, **7.** K, **8.** F, **9.** G, **10.** L, **11.** J, **12.** B, **13.** C, **14.** M, **15.** I

**MAMMALS: GROUPS AND TRAITS, page 13**

| ACROSS | DOWN |
|---|---|
| 2. INSECTIVORE | 1. PELAGE |
| 7. LAGOMORPHS | 3. ECHOLOCATION |
| 9. MONOTREME | 4. EDENTATES |
| 10. CARNIVORE | 5. PLACENTA |
| 11. CETACEANS | 6. RODENTS |
| 12. DENTITION | 8. OMNIVORE |
| 15. UNGULATES | 12. DIAPHRAGM |
| 16. HERBIVORE | 13. MAMMAL |
| 17. MARSUPIAL | 14. PRIMATES |
| 18. GESTATION | |
| 19. UTERUS | |

**BIRD ADAPTATIONS, page 14**

1. The bird's body is adapted to provide low weight and high power. The skeleton is very light, with hollow bones and criss-cross reinforcing inside for wings and tail, providing high surface area and low weight for fanning the air and gliding. There are numerous air sacs within the body. Birds have no urinary bladder, so they don't store wastes. The reproductive organs are reduced and eggs are not stored internally. Birds have a high body temperature and metabolic rate, with powerful wing muscles that make up half their body weight. Only oxygenated blood is pumped through the body and the heart is large and powerful. The bird's respiratory system is also well developed.
2. Contour feathers are large feathers that give the bird its contour or outline, streamlining the animal. They form most of the wing and tail, providing most of the flight surfaces.
   Down feathers are short, fluffy feathers that cover the young chicks and in adults are underneath the contour feathers. They provide insulation.
   Filoplumes–these are sparsely scattered feathers with few barbs, usually at the tip and a long shaft.These usually are found around the base of contour feathers and give extra insulation.

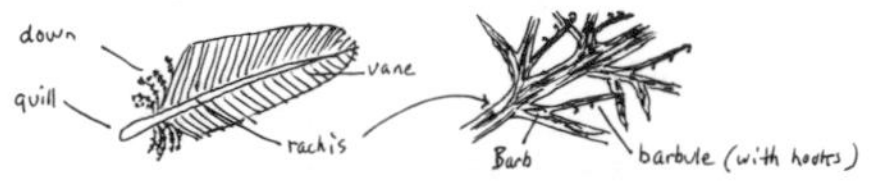


3. They exhibit territoriality, which means staking out a particular area to defend, especially during breeding. They can show courtship behavior to attract a mate and take care of their young at different levels. Their feet, body type, and bills have adapted to their environments and what they feed upon. A duck may have webbed feet and a flat bill, while a woodpecker has feet that curve to hold on to trees and a sharp, pointed beak for digging out insects. Many birds also migrate seasonally, navigating by sun, stars, and the earth's magnetic field.

**MAMMAL BEHAVIOR, page 15**

1. Migration is an instinctive seasonal movement of animals from one place to another. Usually this is due to reduced food supplies or weather conditions. Examples are caribou migrating to winter feeding grounds, whales moving from the Arctic to the tropics during winter, and elk and deer moving out of the high country during winter.
2. Hibernation is a deep state of sleep when animals' metabolic rate slows down and body temperature drops. The hibernating animal lives on stored body fat. Some hibernating animals, like squirrels, wake up at times and eat stored food. The brown bear is not in true hibernation, though it does achieve a drowsy state and is inactive. Other mammals may remain in a deep sleep for almost six months.
3. Territoriality is the marking and defending of the territory where an animal or group of animals live against others of the same species. Mammals who are territorial include rabbits, wolves, sea lions, and cougars.
4. Social hierarchy is a ranking among members of a group of animals that live and work together, usually achieved through threats and fights among the older males. Once a ranking is established, further fighting is minimized. Submission and dominance gestures help maintain this hierarchy until a submissive individual feels ready to challenge a higher ranked member of the group. Common examples are wolves in a pack and baboons in a troop. With baboons, their hierarchy is of particular value because the females and young are surrounded and guarded by the larger adult males.
5. Courtship behavior is a pattern of behavior and rituals used to attract a mate, usually performed by the male. The female responds in different ways to accept or refuse the male. Courtship behavior may establish a bond between two mates. Mammals exhibiting courtship behavior range from hamsters to horses.
6. Communication - Mammals communicate via signals that include odors, sounds, touching, and visual displays, such as an ear motion in a horse, or the tail of a skunk rising. A beaver may warn others of danger with a slap of its tail on the water, and the hair standing on a wolf's neck, or a snarl, conveys a message to back off. Whales 'sing' to convey information, and humans and chimpanzees can communicate via sign language (once learned).

**VERTEBRATE COMPARISONS, page 16**

1. Some fish have cartilage skeletons. All other vertebrates have bone, with some cartilage. All embryos have notochords, though only jawless fish keep them. The vertebrae of land animals interlock. Those in fishes do not. The pectoral and pelvic girdles are much larger in land vertebrates. The size and shape of particular bones like the skull may vary widely.
2. Three types of muscles are found: skeletal or voluntary, smooth or involuntary, and cardiac or heart muscles. In fishes, the main skeletal muscles are made of myomeres, or blocks, which alternately contract or relax. In most land animals, there are more limb muscles, usually in pairs. One muscle's action is opposite the other's.
3. The skin, or outer covering, varies. In fish, the skin is covered with scales. With sharks, the scales may have toothlike spines. Keratin hardens the skins of many sharks and rays. Amphibians have thin skins and mucous glands. Reptiles have dry scales. Even birds have scales on their legs and feathers over the skin. Mammals have hair and a layer of fat in the skin for insulation and sweat glands. Birds and mammals have skin that produces beaks, claws, nails, and horns.
4. Vertebrates have the "tube within a tube" plan. The internal tube is the digestive system. Digestion is usually outside the cells, within body cavities. The digestive systems of plant eaters are adapted to digesting cellulose. Many plant eaters have special grinding teeth and long digestive tracts with microbes for breaking down cellulose. Ceca, or blind sacs in the digestive system trap food, allowing microbes to act. Birds have crops and gizzards. Meat eaters have shorter digestive systems because meat digests easier. All vertebrates have digestive enzymes.
5. Fish have two-chambered hearts and amphibians three. Most reptiles have three-chambered hearts. Alligators, crocodiles, birds, and mammals all have four-chambered hearts. All systems are closed systems with blood, blood vessels, and a heart. Fish have a single circuit blood pathway. Most amphibians, reptiles, and all mammals have a double circuit pathway, which takes blood through the heart, to the lungs, back to the heart, and then through the body.
6. In fish and stages of amphibians where gills are present, gas exchange is through the gills, which are rich in capillaries. Amphibians also exchange gases through their skin. Moisture is necessary for gills and skin absorption. With internal lungs there is not a drying problem. The larger or more active the animal, the more gas exchange surface needed, hence the larger lungs of birds and mammals.

**THEM BONES, page 17**

**1.** E, O, J; **2.** C, H, D, N; **3.** M, G, I; **4.** I, A, F; **5.** B; **6.** L, K

**THE HUMAN BODY: SKELETON AND MAJOR TISSUES, page 17**

1. epithelial, connective, muscle, nervous
2. axial and appendicular
3. The cartilage and fibrous tissue membranes in the embryo skeleton are slowly replaced by bone.
4. compact bone tissue, spongy bone tissue, and marrow
5. skeletal, smooth, and cardiac
6. Paired muscles work in opposition to one another, one contracts while the other relaxes, working as a lever.
7. Muscle fibers are made of myofibrils, which in turn are made of myosin and actin filaments. When a muscle contracts, the actin filaments slide past the myosin filaments.
8. From the conversion of ATP to ADP+P in the cells of the muscle fibers
9. the epidermis and the dermis
10. protecting the body, regulating the body temperature, sensing the environment, excreting waste, and synthesizing vitamin D

**TAKE YOUR VITAMINS, page 18**

1. Thiamine: oxidation of carbohydrates, nerve and muscle function: whole grain foods, wheat germ, eggs, potatoes, meats, yeast, milk
2. Riboflavin: cell respiration, healthy skin and eyes: milk, eggs, meats, wheat germ, green vegetables
3. Niacin: Cell respiration: meats, fish, liver, whole grain, peanuts, yeast
4. Vitamin $B_{12}$: development of red blood cells: meats, milk, liver
5. Ascorbic Acid: healthy bones and teeth, strength of capillaries, aids healing: citrus and other fruits, tomatoes, peppers, leafy green vegetables
6. Vitamin A: healthy linings of respiratory, digestive, excretory and reproductive systems, healthy eyes: dairy products, egg yolk, fish-liver oil, green and yellow vegetables
7. Vitamin D: growth and development of bones and teeth, metabolism of calcium and phosphorus: fortified dairy products, fish-liver oil, saltwater fish
8. Tocopherol: maintaining fat component of cell membranes: wheat germ oil, leafy green

vegetables, meats, egg yolk

9. Vitamin K: normal blood clotting and liver function: leafy green vegetables, cauliflower, also produced by intestinal bacteria

**MINERAL WEALTH AND HEALTH, page 19**

1. Zinc: beans, liver, lentils, spinach, many other foods
2. Copper: liver and meats, oysters, shrimp, peas, pecans
3. Chlorine: table salt, many foods
4. Sodium: table salt, seafood, many foods
5. Magnesium: green vegetables, beans, bran, corn, peanuts, meat, milk
6. Iodine: iodized salt, saltwater fish, oysters, shrimp, broccoli
7. Iron: liver, eggs, nuts, legumes, raisins
8. Potassium: beans, bran, potatoes, bananas, apricots
9. Phosphorus: dairy products, meats, legumes, whole grains
10. Calcium: dairy products, eggs, fish, legumes

**LUNCH FROM THE INSIDE, page 20**

| ACROSS | DOWN |
|---|---|
| 2. LIVER | 1. PERISTALSIS |
| 5. EPIGLOTTIS | 3. ESOPHAGUS |
| 8. CANINES | 4. PANCREAS |
| 10. MOLARS | 6. SPHINCTERS |
| 11. BILE | 7. DUODENUM |
| 13. APPENDIX | 8. COLON |
| 15. CEMENTUM | 9. CHYME |
| 16. PHARYNX | 10. MOUTH |
| 17. INCISORS | 12. JEJUNUM |
| 19. STOMACH | 14. RECTUM |
| 22. ILEUM | 18. SALIVA |
| 23. ENAMEL | 20. CECUM |
| | 21. DENTIN |

**THE COMPOSITION AND FUNCTIONS OF BLOOD, page 21**

1. Red blood cells are also called erythrocytes. They are the most numerous, supply oxygen to the blood, are very small and structurally simple with no nucleus or organelles. They contain the red pigment hemoglobin which binds and carries oxygen. They are produced in the bone marrow and live about 120 days. When they pass through blood vessels in the lungs, they collect oxygen and later, in other parts of the body, give up that oxygen to tissues needing it. The spleen removes old and damaged RBCs from circulation and stores some reserve supplies of healthy RBCs.
2. White blood cells are larger and less numerous than RBCs. Another name for white blood cells is leukocytes. They are more complex and may circulate in the blood or leave and enter other tissues, where they may live for many years. A granulocyte is named for the many granules in its cytoplasm. These irregular-shaped cells are the most numerous of the white cells and are active phagocytes, which are attracted to and destroy bacteria and other foreign matter. Monocytes have a large nucleus and few granules. They are slower to respond than granulocytes but are capable of destroying many more bacteria by phagocytosis. When found outside the blood in other tissues, the monocytes may change into macrophages. The third type of white blood cells are lymphocytes, which are involved in the immune response. White blood cells are associated with pus, which is a mixture of white cells, dead bacteria, and the remains of dead cells. Granulocytes and monocytes are produced in the bone marrow, but lymphocytes are made in several places in the body. Many white blood cells live under the skin and around the lungs and digestive system.
3. More than half the blood is fluid. Plasma is mostly water, but contains dissolved proteins, enzymes, simple food materials, waste products, and some chemicals which act as buffers. Buffers help prevent changes in the pH of blood, which is around 7.4.
4. Platelets are also called thrombocytes and are cell fragments released into the blood by cells in the bone marrow. There are granules in the center of each platelet. Several substances including ADP are in the granules. When a blood vessel is damaged, nearby platelets release their stored ADP, which causes the platelets to become sticky. This helps plug the gap in the damaged blood vessels. Fibrin forms to help hold the clotting platelets together, forming a plug. Eventually the fibrin threads in the clot shrinks, pulling the sides in the broken blood vessel back together.

**JUST YOUR TYPE, page 21**

The names of the four types are based on the name of the antigen on the surface of the red blood cells. An antigen is a substance that causes antibodies to be made. The antigens on red blood cells result in different surface features on the cells.

Type A blood has antigen A on the surfaces of red blood cells.

Type B blood has antigen B on the surfaces of red blood cells.

Type AB blood has both antigens, A and B, on their RBC (red blood cell) surfaces. Type O blood has neither A nor B antigens on their RBCs. Most people have antibodies in their plasma against the blood type antigens they DO NOT have. Type A blood has an antibody against B antigen. Type B blood has an antibody against A antigen. Type AB blood doesn't have either antibody. Type O blood has antibodies against both A and B antigen.

The interaction between antigen and antibody causes the blood to clump. To type blood, add antibody A and antibody B to two drops of blood. If both drops of blood clump, the blood type is AB. If neither drop of blood clumps, the blood type is O. If the only drop clumping received antibody A, the blood type is A. If the only drop clumping received antibody B, the blood type is B.

A patient with AB blood can receive any type of blood. A patient with A, B, or O blood can only receive their own type.

The Rh factor, named after the rhesus monkey, where it was first found, is another antigen found on the red blood cells of about 85% of the U.S. population. Those with this antigen are Rh-positive, those without it are Rh-negative. Problems occur when an Rh-negative mother has a second child who also carries the Rh-positive factor. The developing fetus may be contaminated by the mother's blood, which has produced antibodies against Rh-positive blood. The baby's blood cells could be destroyed by her antibodies.

**DON'T WASTE YOUR BREATH, page 22**

| ACROSS | DOWN |
|---|---|
| 1. HYPOXIA | 2. ALVEOLI |
| 6. ASTHMA | 3. TRACHEA |
| 7. BRONCHI | 4. EMPHYSEMA |
| 8. LUNGS | 5. LARYNX |
| 9. EPIGLOTTIS | 10. INSPIRATION |
| 12. RESPIRATION | 11. PNEUMONIA |
| 13. PLEURA | |
| 14. EXPIRATION | |
| 15. DIAPHRAGM | |
| 16. SINUSES | |
| 17. BRONCHIOLES | |

**THE KIDNEYS, page 23**

**1.** excretion, **2.** urea, **3.** kidneys, **4.** urine, **5.** ureters, **6.** urethra, **7.** nephrons, **8.** glomerulus, **9.** Bowman's capsule, **10.** proximal convoluted tubule, **11.** Henle's loop, **12.** distal convoluted tubule, **13.** cortex, **14.** medulla, **15.** glomerular filtrate, **16.** antidiuretic hormone, **17.** diuresis, **18.** hemodialysis

**THE NERVES OF US, page 24**

1. brain and spinal cord
2. the nerves that extend from the brain and spinal cord to all parts of the body
3. A voluntary response is one under conscious control from the central nervous system (moving skeletal muscles). An involuntary response occurs automatically (digesting food).
4. the cerebrum: conscious sensation and voluntary body control; the cerebellum: coordination of muscular activities; the brain stem: internal functions, heartbeat
5. the specialized cells of the nervous system, composed of the cell body, dendrites, and axons
6. the smallest stimulus that can produce an action potential
7. potassium and sodium
8. a gap between neurons that a nerve impulse must cross
9. When a neuron is stimulated, an impulse is conducted from the point of stimulus to the opposite end of a neuron. The stimulation causes the cell membrane to change suddenly, becoming permeable to sodium ions. These ions diffuse inward, causing the neuron, at that point, to become depolarized. This depolarization passes down the neuron in a wave, which is called the action potential. This action potential, (wave) is the nerve impulse. When it reaches an axon ending, there is a synapse. While the nerve impulse so far has been electrical, the crossing of a synapse is a chemical reaction involving neurotransmitters.
10. An axon is an extension of the neuron that carries nerve impulses away from the cell body. A dendron is an extension of the neuron that carries impulses toward the cell body.

**THE OTHER CONTROL SYSTEM: ENDOCRINE, page 25**

1. growth hormone; necessary for normal growth prolactin: milk production in females
2. oxytocin; uterus contractions during childbirth antidiuretic hormone; reabsorption of water - kidneys
3. thyroxin; metabolic rate calcitonin; regulates blood calcium and phosphorus
4. parathyroid hormone; works with calcitonin
5. adrenaline; response to stress and exertion
6. corticosteroids; reduce inflammation
7. estrogen; female sex hormones progesterone; prepares uterus for pregnancy
8. testosterone; male sex hormone
9. insulin; reduce sugar levels glucagon; increase sugar levels
10. thymic hormone; regulate lymphocyte production
11. melatonin; release of FSH and LH (sexual maturity)

**ECOLOGY AND THE ENVIRONMENT, page 26**

| ACROSS | DOWN |
|---|---|
| 1. PRODUCERS | 2. DENITRIFICATION |
| 4. CARNIVORES | 3. HABITAT |
| 6. NITRIFICATION | 5. AUTOTROPHS |
| 7. POPULATION | 10. ECOSYSTEM |
| 8. PRECIPITATION | 11. DECOMPOSERS |
| 9. HERBIVORES | 13. CONDENSATION |
| 12. NICHE | 15. PARASITISM |
| 14. EVAPORATION | 20. CONSUMERS |
| 16. AMMONIFICATION | 21. MUTUALISM |
| 17. SOIL | 22. HUMIDITY |
| 18. COMMENSALISM | 25. BIOSPHERE |
| 19. OMNIVORES | |
| 23. COMMUNITY | |
| 24. SYMBIOSIS | |
| 26. CLIMATE | |
| 27. ECOLOGY | |

**BIOTIC POTENTIAL - HOW MUCH DO YOU LIKE GREEN?, page 27**

**NOTE TO TEACHER:** Bell peppers could be cut in half to cut costs or use cherry tomatoes or some readily available fruit with plenty of seeds.

1–5 Answers will vary.

Sample graph based on 100 seeds per pepper:

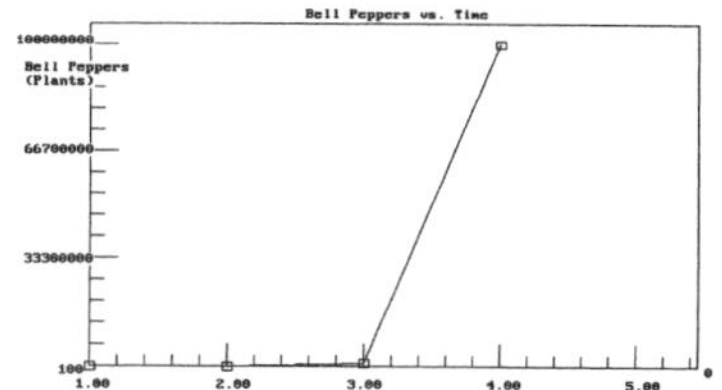

6. Answers will vary. It is common and produces a lot of seeds.
7. Water, soil, room to grow, pests, diseases, etc.
8. Carrying capacity is the population size of a species that an environment can support. Bell peppers are easier to control than flies, have greater requirements, need more room. etc.
9. Answers will vary. The earth has limited resources.

**ECHINODERMS, page 29**

**1.** D, **2.** K, **3.** C, **4.** A, **5.** B, **6.** E, **7.** H, **8.** J, **9.** L, **10.** G, **11.** F, **12.** M, **13.** I

**THE MOST SUCCESSFUL: THE ARTHROPODS, page 30**

1. A segmented body, an exoskeleton of chitin, and pairs of jointed appendages.
2. Virtually everywhere, from arctic waters to the driest, hottest deserts on earth. They are found in every environment and even inside other living organisms as parasites.
3. This group includes the eight legged carnivorous spiders, tiny parasitic ticks and mites that feed on blood and dead skin, and scorpions, characterized by their lobster-like pedipalps and curved abdomen with venomous barb.
4. The exoskeleton protects the internal organs from predators, and prevents water loss from the body, allowing the organism to survive in dry climates.
5. They have adapted to virtually all of the earth's environments, have a very high productive rate, and reproduce frequently.
6. A crayfish has basically the same body parts and appearance as a lobster, but is smaller and found in fresh water.
7. Both organisms live on land and have long, slender bodies with segments. Abdominal segments have a single pair of legs. Both have heads with two clusters of simple eyes. Centipedes are predators of insects. Millipedes feed mainly on decaying organic matter. Centipedes have modified appendages that serve as poison claws. Millipedes have a pair of antennae, a pair of mandibles, and some of the body segments are fused double segments, which result in two pairs of walking legs.
8. They have a head, thorax, and abdomen, each with a pair of legs. On the head are usually antennae, mandibles and other mouth parts, two compound eyes, and three simple eyes. Some insects have wings.
9. In incomplete metamorphosis, eggs laid by an adult female develop into a nymph, which grows into adulthood. In complete metamorphosis, an egg develops into a larva, a pupa, and eventually into an adult.
10. By movement patterns, behavior, and special scents or pheromones.

**DESIGNER INSECTS, page 31**

Drawings will vary. Make sure each insect structure is labeled and the donating insect identified.

**BEHAVIOR AND ADAPTATIONS IN ARTHROPODS, page 32**

Answers may include:

1. social organization, modifications as worker, drone, and queen, specialized movements or dances to show direction of food, nurturing of young, protection of the hive
2. modified mouth parts for soldiers, formic acid to sting enemies, social structure with workers soldiers, queen, nest, scents to lead others to food
3. modified mouth parts for siphoning, mimicry to fool enemies and hide, different food supply for larva and adult, complete metamorphosis in reproduction
4. modified mouth parts for piercing and sucking blood, chemicals in saliva to slow blood clotting
5. production of silk to form webs to trap prey, able to feel vibrations of prey on web, courtship displays to attract mate, some able to build houses underwater, trapping oxygen in their hairs, some have poison to paralyze prey
6. able to digest cellulose, modified mouthparts for tunneling into wood, social structure with queen, soldiers

**LIFE IN A HONEYBEE SOCIETY, page 33**

1. The queen is the only fertile female in the hive. Her only job is to reproduce. While still a larva, she's fed royal jelly by nurse bees. After she emerges from the pupa, she flies off, mates with a male drone, then returns to the hive and starts laying eggs. Nurse bees continue to feed her royal jelly as long as she lives, which may be for several years.
2. The males, or drones, emerge from unfertilized eggs. Their only job is to mate with the queen. They cannot feed themselves and after the end of the summer they are driven off and soon starve to death.
3. The workers in the hive are sterile females. They do all the jobs in the hive except reproduction. Once out of the pupa, the worker becomes a nurse bee, feeding and tending the larva, drones, and queen by secreting royal jelly. At middle age, the bees secrete wax instead. They clean, repair, and build the hive and guard the entrance. Once they get old, they go and forage for pollen and nectar, which they bring back to the hive. They relate the information about food source locations by performing one of two types of dances for other workers. The first of these, the round dance, communicates that nectar is relatively close to the hive. The second, the waggle dance, gives not only the information of a further distance to the food source, but also the direction from the hive. Workers continue to forage until they die. Female workers usually live less than six weeks.

**INVERTEBRATES: COMPARING BODY SYSTEMS, page 34**

**1.** A, B, C, **2.** C, **3.** E, F, G, H, I, J, **4.** G, I, H, J, **5.** E, F, G, **6.** H, I, J, **7.** I, **8.** H, **9.** J, **10.** F, G, H, J, **11.** C, D, B, E, F, H, **12.** G, I, J, **13.** G, J, I (some), **14.** A, B, C, D, E, J (some), **15.** H, J, I

**WHAT ARE THE CHORDATES?, page 35**

1. Chordates must have a notochord, a slim flexible rod that supports the body. They also must have a dorsal nerve chord and gill slits at some time during the life cycle.
2. Urochordata are the tunicates. They have a tunic or tough outer coating made of a substance similar to cellulose. Tunicates live in sea water and most are sessile as adults, unable to move. They many be found at great depths on the ocean floor. Some live in colonies.
   Cephalochordata are the lancets. They live in warm seas, mostly in burrows in mud or sand, with only their mouths sticking out. Cilia in their mouths create currents which move water past them and the lancets strain food out through the gills. Like the tunicates, the lancets have no distinct brain.
   Vertebrates all have a vertebrae or backbone enclosing and protecting a spinal cord. All have an endoskeleton either of cartilage or bone. The skeleton grows along with the organism, and is not shed. Individual classes within this phylum include fish, amphibians, reptiles, birds, and mammals.
3. Drawings will vary.

**FISH OR FROGS?, page 36**

1. Fish, Frogs (not exclusively)
2. Fish, Frogs (during tadpole stage only)
3. Frogs (not exclusively)
4. Fish (one group)
5. Fish (one group), Frogs
6. Frogs
7. Fish, Frogs (during tadpole stage only)
8. Fish (not all)
9. Fish
10. Frogs
11. Fish (not all)
12. Fish
13. Frogs, Fish (lungfish only)
14. Fish, Frogs (tadpole stage only)
15. Fish, Frogs
16. Fish (some species), Frogs
17. Neither

**REPTILES, page 37**

| ACROSS | DOWN |
|---|---|
| 1. OVIPAROUS | 2. ALLANTOIS |
| 4. CARAPACE | 3. HEMOTOXIN |
| 5. ECTOTHERM | 6. REPTILES |
| 7. VIVIPAROUS | 8. PLASTRON |
| 9. TUATARA | 10. AMNION |
| 11. AMNIOTE | 12. SHELL |
| 14. CHORION | 13. YOLK |

**REPTILE VOCABULARY QUIZ, page 38**

**1.** chorion, **2.** reptiles, **3.** amniote, **4.** allantois, **5.** tuatara, **6.** ectotherm, **7.** hemotoxin, **8.** plastron, **9.** shell, **10.** amnion, **11.** carapace, **12.** yolk, **13.** viviparous, **14.** oviparous

**TRANSPORT FOR PLANTS, page 39**

| ACROSS | DOWN |
|---|---|
| 1. TRANSPIRATION | 1. TRANSLOCATION |
| 2. GUTTATION | 3. CAPILLARITY |
| 4. DIFFUSION | 5. HALOPHYTE |
| 5. HYDROTROPISM | 6. COHESION |
| 7. SAP | 9. OSMOSIS |
| 8. WILTING | 12. GIRDLING |
| 10. XEROPHYTE | |
| 11. ADHESION | |
| 13. TURGOR | |
| 14. VESSELS | |
| 15. SUCCULENT | |

**MEASURING TRANSPIRATION IN LEAVES: PART 2 page 41**

1. The water came from the leaves.
2. The bag placed in sunlight probably produced the most moisture.
3. Answers should include sunlight and temperature.
4. Variability between leaves, moisture in the air, outside temperature, room conditions, measuring errors, opening and closing the bag, etc.
5. The leaves with the greatest total mass probably contained the most water, unless the mass of each group of 10 leaves was identical. The purpose was to determine which condition caused transpiration to increase the most.

**REPRODUCTION IN PLANTS, page 42**

**1.** L, **2.** A, **3.** B, **4.** J, **5.** N, **6.** M, **7.** O, **8.** G, **9.** P, **10.** Q, **11.** I, **12.** S, **13.** T, **14.** U, **15.** H, **16.** V, **17.** W, **18.** R, **19.** K, **20.** F, **21.** C, **22.** D, **23.** E

**EXPLAINING PLANT REPRODUCTION, page 43**

1. When the pollen grain comes into contact with the female gametophyte, special proteins are activated and a pollen tube grows from the pollen grain to the ovule. Sperm cells move from the pollen grain down the tube, reaching an egg in the ovule. One sperm unites with the egg to form a zygote. After this, the zygote can develop into a seed.
2. When conditions are right: the correct amount of heat, water, and oxygen, a viable seed may become active, absorbing water and swelling. The radicle grows and the seed coat breaks. The embryo digests food from the cotyledons and the radicle develops roots. The hypocotyl and the cotyledons push their way to the surface of the soil. The leaves began to make sugar through photosynthesis. As food is used, the cotyledons shrivel up and the seed coat drops off. The seedling becomes self sufficient as it grows and develops.
3. Pollination is the transfer of pollen from the anther of a stamen to the stigma of a pistil. It may be aided by wind, insects, birds, or other living things. If pollen is transferred to a flower of the same species, fertilization may be the next step.
4. Fruits may aid in seed dispersal, the spreading of seeds to other locations where they may find suitable conditions and germinate. Animals may carry the fruit to other locations or eat it at there, excreting the undigested seeds. Other fruits have sticky hooks and are carried by animals accidentally to new location, like burrs and thistle. Some seeds are carried by the wind and may have wings. Others may be carried by water or explode and scatter when they are ripe. The further a seed is carried away from others of its type, the less competition it will have for resources when it germinates.
5. Natural vegetative propagation includes all asexual processes that occur naturally. Examples are the runners of plants, like strawberries, which develop into new plants. Other plants, like white potatoes, reproduce from rhizomes. Bulbs, corms, and roots can also develop new plants directly in some species. Gardeners can grow new plants from cuttings (a leaf and stem allowed to root in water), layering (bending the tip of a plant into the ground again), and by grafting plant parts onto others, as is done commonly with trees.

**FACTORS THAT AFFECT PLANT GROWTH, page 43**

**1.** C, **2.** B, **3.** D, **4.** A, **5.** F, **6.** E

**Some responses might be:**

Air movement: Trees growing at high altitude or area where high winds are common often have branches and leaves on one side of the tree. Chemical factors: carbon dioxide and oxygen must be present in sufficient amounts and compounds in the soil, like salt, can restrict growth. Air pollution is another chemical factor to consider. Plant-produced chemicals: some plants release chemicals that create zones around them that prevent other plants from growing. Room to grow: the number of surrounding plants can limit growth and the presence of these plants can reduce the amount of light available. Length of light: seasonal amounts of light available, called photoperiodism, the number of light and dark hours in the day is a growth factor for many plants, especially in flower development.

**PLANT RESPONSES AND BEHAVIOR, page 44**

Sketches will vary.

1. The positive growth of a plant toward light.
2. The growth of a part of a plant toward or away from gravity. A stem might grow away from gravity and a root toward it.
3. A part of a plant, like a pollen tube, growing toward the ovule, in response to a chemical signal.
4. The response of vines, first touching, then encircling objects, like a vine growing up a tree.

**CHARTING SIMPLE INVERTEBRATES, page 45**

**Sponges:** none; none, filter feeders; none; choanocyte captures food particles, cells ingest food; aquatic, mostly marine; asexually by buds or sexually, some are hermaphrodites

**Hydra:** radial; mouth and gastrovascular cavity; branching nerve net, no brain; catches prey with nematocysts, moved into mouth via tentacles; freshwater ponds; asexually by buds or sexually, hermaphroditic

**Flatworm:** bilateral; mouth, pharynx, gastrovascular cavity; two main nerve cords with branches, ganglia serve as brain; carnivorous, feed through mouth; usually aquatic, some in damp soil; asexually by fission or sexually, hermaphroditic.

**Flukes:** bilateral; poorly developed, pharynx and intestine; nerve cords and ganglia; parasitic inside host; various hosts during life cycle; eggs in water, pass to host snail, various stages and hosts, end up in human (liver fluke)

**Tapeworm:** bilateral, body sections called proglottids; none, absorbs food directly, parasitic; nerve cords and ganglia; absorbs food directly from intestine of host; various hosts during life cycle; hermaphroditic or sperm transfer between individuals.

**Roundworm:** bilateral; complete with mouth and anus; nerve cords and ganglia; free living or parasitic; freshwater, soil, mud, rotting organisms; sexual in some species

**Earthworm:** bilateral, segmented; complete with mouth and anus and other specialized regions; brain, nerve cords and branches; mouth and muscular pharynx; soil, fresh and salt water; sexual or hermaphroditic

**CORAL REEFS, page 46**

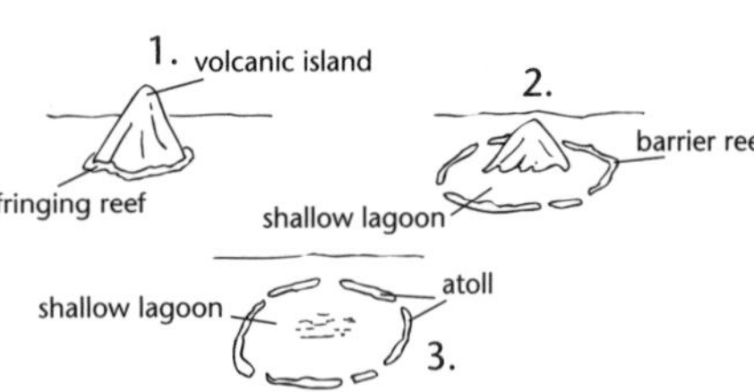


1. In a fringing reef, the coral is closely attached to the shore or land mass.
2. A barrier reef forms some distance off shore with a shallow lagoon between.
3. In an atoll, a barrier reef may continue to grow in shallow waters if the organisms survive. The island may disappear, leaving a shallow lagoon in the center. Atolls may be V-shaped.
4. In going from fringing to barrier to atoll, a sequence of volcanic islands form, then the beginning of a reef. As the volcano becomes inactive and subsides, the barrier reef forms and eventually results in an atoll.
5. This mountain range in SE New Mexico forms the edges of a great barrier reef that once bordered an ancient shallow sea.
6. The Great Barrier Reef extends for nearly 1,300 miles along the northeastern coast of Australia. It is the world's largest coral reef and includes hundreds of small islands.

**MOLLUSKS CHART, page 47**

Class pelecypoda: characterized by a compressed body, no head, a wedge-shaped muscular foot for digging and a two-part (bivalve) hinged shell covering the body. Members are clams, oysters, and mussels.

Class gastropoda: characterized by a head with eyes, tentacles, and a large flat foot for creeping. A coiled, one-part shell (univalve)is usually present. Members are snails and slugs.

Class Cephalopoda: characterized by a head with eyes. The foot is divided into arms or tentacles used for grabbing, swimming, etc. Shells may be absent, present, or present but internal. Members are squids, cuttlefish, and octopuses.

Class Amphineura: has a small head with no eyes or tentacles and a large, flat adhesive foot. The shell is composed of eight dorsal plates. Chitons are members of this small class.

1. Crawling on the muscular foot, swimming or walking via tentacles, forcing water out by closing the shells rapidly, creeping along a thread-like substance secreted, and forcing jets of water out the siphon.
2. esophagus, heart, kidney, liver, stomach, intestine
3. They have very large, easy to study nerve fibers and they can learn.

4. Shellfish and snails for food, pearls, ink (sepia), shells used for many things, including fill for roadbeds. Many mollusks, especially those that feed on wood or serve as hosts for parasites, are harmful economically.
5. The presence, shape, and number of shells.

**MONERANS AND VIRUSES, page 48**

1. A virus is a particle with a nuclei acid core surrounded by a coat or capsid of protein.
2. The nucleic acid contains the code containing the information about what kind of virus it is.
3. A virus has only one nucleic acid and does not have a cellular structure. It is much smaller, and cannot reproduce itself like a prokaryotic cell can. A virus must get what it needs inside a living cell. A bacteria has a cell membrane, cytoplasm, and protein enzymes needed for simple processes.
4. Viroids are much smaller than viruses, which makes them even harder to detect and study.
5. They are autotrophs, making their own food through photosynthesis and contain chlorophyll. They don't contain chloroplasts, mitochondria, large vacuoles, or other membrane-bound organelles.
6. They are helpful in that they attack bacteria, not humans and are so large they are much easier to study than other viruses. They, and the bacteria they attack, are easy to grow and study in the lab.
7. They are widely studied because they are large, reproduce quickly, and attack bacteria, which are also easily grown and studied. Most of our knowledge of viruses comes from phages.
8. Bacteria grow best in warm, damp places with plenty of organic matter. Sewage is an excellent growth medium.
9. Bacteria decompose many materials in the environment, supplying carbon, nitrogen, and other important elements. They fix nitrogen, needed by plants and live inside and help humans and animals by aiding in digestion. They also cause the production of cheese, yogurt, vinegar, and other food products. The study of bacteria has helped us in making antibiotics and other medicines.
10. Obligate aerobes require oxygen for respiration and obligate anaerobes can only grow when oxygen is not present.
11. Binary fission is the splitting of a cell after nuclear material duplicates. Two cells are formed after a membrane grows between the two sets of nuclear material. In conjugation, genetic material is transferred from one bacterial cell to another by direct contact between the cells.
12. Monerans are typically one-celled prokaryotes that lack a nucleus or membrane-bound organelles. They are usually much smaller than eukaryote cells.

**THE HUMAN BODY'S BARRIERS TO INFECTION, page 49**

Answers will vary.

1. LARGE INTESTINE: has large population of harmless bacteria, which prevent growth of harmful species.
2. LIVER: has role in wound repair and produces some blood-clotting factors.
3. LYMPH NODES: glands produce lymphocytes, which produce antibodies and digest bacteria.
4. LYMPHATIC SYSTEM: conducts lymph throughout body, carrying bacteria to lymph nodes, where it can be destroyed.
5. SKIN: provides a physical barrier to pathogens.
6. SMALL INTESTINE: relatively free of bacteria because food entering has been cleansed by gastric juices.
7. SPLEEN: produces white blood cells, which remove unwanted materials from blood.
8. STOMACH: secretes strong acids which kill bacteria in food ingested.
9. TEAR GLANDS: chemicals in tears kill bacteria and wash dust out of eyes.

**DISEASES AND MICROBES, page 50**

**1.** E, **2.** C, **3.** F, **4.** G, **5.** H, **6.** I, **7.** K, **8.** L, **9.** O, **10.** J, **11.** B, **12.** A, **13.** M, **14.** N, **15.** D

**VASCULAR OR NON-VASCULAR PLANTS, page 51**

**1.** NV, **2.** NV, **3.** NV, **4.** V, **5.** V, **6.** V, **7.** V, **8.** V, **9.** NV, **10.** NV, **11.** NV, **12.** NV, **13.** V,

**ALGAE: RED, GREEN, OR BROWN?, page 52**

Green algae: mostly fresh water, but also salt water, snow, soil, and trees; all three; sexually by conjugation, asexually, or both; maybe motile through flagella, some have holdfasts, forms plankton with other organisms; Chlamydomonas, Volvox, Chlorella, Spirogyra

Red algae: mostly marine plants; all, but most are multicellular; complex life cycles with alteration of generation, specialized sperm and egg structures, special pigments allow deep growth, provides agar and carrageenin, used for growing microbes and food thickeners; Polysiphonia, Porphyra, Chondrus

Brown algae: mostly marine; all multicellular; life cycles where diploid and haploid plants can be very different; grow rapidly, get quite large, has specialized structure, produces algin, used in making medicine, ice cream, etc. Laminaria, Macrocystis

1. Red algae has certain pigments that can absorb green, violet, and blue light waves, and transfer the absorbed energy to chlorophyll.
2. As food additives, laboratory growth medium (agar), and a food source.

**SEED PLANTS, page 53**

| ACROSS | DOWN |
|---|---|
| 2. VENATION | 1. GINKGOES |
| 4. DICOTS | 3. MONOCOTS |
| 6. ROOT | 5. CYCADS |
| 10. CORK | 7. TUBER |
| 11. EPIDERMIS | 8. GYMNOSPERMS |
| 13. CONIFERS | 9. BLADE |
| 14. STELE | 12. STOMATA |
| 15. PETIOLE | 17. VEINS |
| 16. LEAF | 18. BARK |
| 19. ANGIOSPERMS | |
| 20. STEM | |

**GETTING TO THE ROOT OF GREEN PLANTS, page 54**

Drawings will vary.

1. Trees in swamps may develop adventitious roots above the ground, prop roots, to give added support to the plant. They also absorb oxygen, something the primary roots below water cannot do.
2. Bacteria grow within these nodules, fixing nitrogen, which is placed into a chemical form useful for the plant. Nitrogen is an important component of proteins and the plant benefits. When these plants die, the nitrogen they leave behind enriches the soil for future plantings.

**LEARNING LEAVES, page 55**

Drawings will vary.

1. The stomata are openings in the leaf which allow water vapor and oxygen to pass out and carbon dioxide to enter
2. They vary in size, smaller leaves losing less water and larger leaves gathering more sunlight. Plants in dry climates have fewer somata. Some plants store water in their leaves. Pea plants have modified leaves which coil around structures to hold them up.

**STEM STUDIES, page 56**

1. Drawings will vary.
2. Color of twig, texture, bud arrangement . . .
3. The stems of some cacti resemble leaves and carry out photosynthesis. They are protected by non-photosynthetic leaves modified into needles. Many store water. Others, like the potato, store food in a modified stem called a tuber. Some plants send out horizontal stems, or stolons, which may give rise to new plants.
4. The vascular tissue of the xylem carries water and minerals up from the roots into the plant and the phloem carries food both up and down the plant.

**PLANT TRANSPORTATION SYSTEMS, page 57**

1. Water moves into the roots across a selectively permeable membrane from an area of greater concentration (in the soil) to an area of lesser concentration.
2. Minerals are brought into the root system when energy is expended to transport the mineral molecules across the cell membrane.
3. Water and minerals, in simple plants, flow from an area of greater concentration to an area of lower concentration. This is a slow process and limits the potential size of the plant.
4. Pressure in the xylem results from the inward movement of water into the root cells from osmosis.
5. Capillarity results when a liquid rises inside a tube of very small diameter through cohesion, the attraction of like molecules, and adhesion, the attraction of unlike molecules.
6. When water evaporates from leaves, a pulling force from this transpiration pulls water up from the roots. A column of water exists because of the cohesion between water molecules.

**REALLY ANCIENT HISTORY, page 58**

**1.** G, **2.** M, **3.** K, **4.** P, **5.** J, **6.** E, **7.** D, **8.** L, **9.** N, **10.** F, **11.** I, **12.** O, **13.** A, **14.** B, **15.** C, **16.** H

**A "BUGGY" CLASSIFICATION KEY, page 59**

Answers will vary.

**FINDING COMMON AND SCIENTIFIC NAMES, page 60**

Answers will vary.

**VIRUSES AND MONERANS, page 61**

| ACROSS | DOWN |
|---|---|
| 2. PARASITE | 1. TRANSFORMATION |
| 5. TRANSDUCTION | 3. CONJUGATION |
| 7. BACTERIOPHAGE | 4. COCCI |
| 9. NUCLEOCAPSID | 6. ENDOSPORE |
| 12. REPLICATION | 8. ADSORPTION |
| 13. ANAEROBES | 10. MYCOPLASMAS |
| 14. BACILLI | 11. MONERANS |
| 16. SPIRILLA | 12. RICKETTSIAS |
| 17. AEROBES | 15. VIRUS |
| 18. PROPHAGE | |
| 19. SAPROBES | |
| 20. VIROIDS | |

**CLASSIFYING VIRUSES, page 62**

**bacterial viruses:** bacteria; rod to complex; absent; DNA; 65-2500nm
**chicken pox virus:** animal; complex; present; DNA; 250nm
**cold virus:** animal; many sided; absent; DNA;
**flu virus:** animal; rod; present; RNA; 100nm long
**herpes virus:** animal; many sided; present; DNA
**polio virus:** animal; many sided; absent; RNA; 20nm
**smallpox virus:** animal; complex; present; DNA; 250nm
**tobacco mosaic virus:** plant; rod; absent; RNA; 300nm long
**yellow fever virus:** animal; many sided; present; RNA; 11nm

10. those that infect bacteria
11. cold, flu
12. chicken pox, cold, flu, herpes, polio, smallpox, yellow fever
13. developed to counter all in answer 3 except cold and herpes

**CLASSIFYING BACTERIA BY SHAPE, page 63**

**1.** spinal meningitis, **2.** tonsillitis, **3.** tetanus, **4.** botulism poisoning, **5.** pneumonia, **6.** boils, **7.** syphilis, **8.** anthrax, **9.** buttermilk, **10.** typhoid fever, **11.** sauerkraut, **12.** Bacillus lactis, **13.** Bacillus tetani, **14.** Streptococcus pyogenes, **15.** Bacillus typhosa, **16.** Staphylococcus aureus, **17.** Streptococcus lactis, **18.** Diplococcus meningitidis, **19.** Treponema pallidum, **20.** Bacillus Anthracis, **21.** Diplococcus pneumoniae, **22.** Bacillus botulinum

**SEARCHING FOR PROTISTS, page 64**

**1.** protists, **2.** protozoans, **3.** euglena, **4.** euglenoid, **5.** eyespot, **6.** diatoms, **7.** plasmodium, **8.** pseudopodia, **9.** radiolarian, **10.** foraminifera, **11.** amoeba, **12.** ectoplasm, **13.** endoplasm, **14.** cyst, **15.** ciliate, **16.** paramecium, **17.** pellicle, **18.** gullet, **19.** conjugation, **20.** trichocysts, **21.** sporozoans, **22.** flagellates

**THE THREE SUBKINGDOMS OF PROTISTS, page 65**

*Myxomycota: slime molds; slime molds; found in cool, shaded areas, growing on moist decaying organic matter, is multicellular in some stages, plasmodium may have many nuclei, may get very large, fruiting bodies
*Euglenophyta: euglenoids; Euglenas; mostly fresh water, move with flagella, no cell wall, make their own food, can detect and move toward light
*Chrysophyta: golden algae; Diatoms; has an overlapping, 2-part shell made of silica, contains chlorophyll and other masking pigments, shells have patterns of evenly spaced lines
*Pyrrophyta: fire algae; Dinoflagellates; mostly marine, usually have 2 flagella, have cellulose in cell walls, most have chlorophyll, red ones cause red tide
*Sarcodina: sarcodines; Amoebas; move with pseudopodia, flowing motion, mostly freshwater, surrounds and engulfs food, may form cysts
*Ciliata: ciliates; Paramecia; move using cilia, maintains flexible shape, moves backward and forward, very fast, rotating, reproduces sexually or asexually, may defend itself with trichocysts
*Sporozoa: sporozoans; Plasmodia; parasitic, no means of locomotion, forms spores, complex life cycles, one form causes malaria
*Mastigophora: flagellates; Trypanosomes; move with one or more flagella, some are parasites, some feed like primitive sponges

**THERE'S A FUNGUS AMONG US, page 66**

| ACROSS | DOWN |
|---|---|
| 1. MYCORRHIZA | 2. ASCOMYCETES |
| 5. MYCELIUM | 3. RHIZOIDS |
| 6. SPORANGIUM | 4. FUNGUS |
| 7. GILLS | 8. SEPTA |
| 9. ZYGOSPORES | 11. OOSPORE |
| 10. ZOOSPORES | 12. STOLONS |
| 13. ASCUS | 14. ANNULUS |
| 15. LICHEN | 16. STYPE |
| 17. HYPHAE | |
| 18. BASIDIA | |

**CELL REPRODUCTION, page 67**

| ACROSS | DOWN |
|---|---|
| 5. CENTROMERE | 1. SPERMATOGENESIS |
| 6. MEIOSIS | 2. METAPHASE |
| 9. MONOPLOID | 3. CHROMATID |
| 10. OOGENESIS | 4. DIPLOID |
| 11. NUCLEOTIDES | 7. CHROMOSOME |
| 12. SYNAPSES | 8. INTERPHASE |
| 15. TELOPHASE | 13. HOMOLOGS |
| 16. PROPHASE | 14. GENE |
| 17. GAMETES | |
| 18. MITOSIS | |
| 19. CYTOKINESIS | |

**DNA REPLICATION AND PROTEIN SYNTHESIS, page 68**

1. 4, 1, 3, 2
2. A. The section of DNA containing the 'code' for the protein untwists and unzips, resulting in the exposing of the nucleotide bases. B. Free RNA nucleotides in the nucleus pair up with the exposed DNA bases. Uracil bonds with adenine and guanine bonds with cytosine. Triplets on the DNA strand will have complementary triplets forming on the mRNA molecule. Each correctly sequenced triplet of nucleotides is called a codon. C. Bonds form between the RNA nucleotides and the mRNA strand separates from the DNA strand. The completed mRNA strand containing the code leaves the nucleus, heading for ribosomes in the cytoplasm.
3. A. One end of a mRNA molecule attaches to a ribosome. B. Transfer RNA molecules in the cytoplasm collect certain amino acids. These tRNA move to the attached mRNA. C. A tRNA with three complementary bases (they are called an anticodon) matches up with the correct codon on the mRNA, holding the amino acid it brought in position. D. The mRNA moves down the ribosome, bringing the next codon into contact with it. The next tRNA moves into position with its amino acid, connecting to the previous amino acid with a peptide bond. E. The first tRNA is released, the next codon moves into place, and the next amino acid is put into position. F. The process from C-E is repeated until the entire pattern on the mRNA is translated, forming a chain of amino acids. This chain of amino acids is the protein the mRNA was coded for.

**COMPARING MITOSIS AND MEIOSIS, page 69**

**1.** MITOSIS, **2.** MITOSIS, **3.** MITOSIS, **4.** MEIOSIS, **5.** MEIOSIS, **6.** MEIOSIS, **7.** MITOSIS, **8.** MITOSIS, **9.** MEIOSIS, **10.** MEIOSIS, **11.** MEIOSIS, **12.** MITOSIS, **13.** MEIOSIS, **14.** MITOSIS

15. In meiosis, the pairing of homologous chromosomes (prophase I) and the failure of the centromeres to split (anaphase I).
16. The embryo would have twice the number of chromosomes needed.
17. It adds to the variability of the daughter cells, resulting in different possible chromosome variations and characteristics of the individuals produced.